稲垣理一郎
Riichiro Inagaki

I drew this on my New Year's cards, since it's the Year of the Rooster.

This was written in 2005. —Ed.

村田雄介
Yusuke Murata

I'm always trying to blow away eraser dust with my mask on.

I get terrible hay fever around this time of year, and I make a fool of myself doing this at least once a week.

Damn hay fever!

Eyeshield 21 is the most exciting football manga to hit the scene. A collaborative effort between writer Riichiro Inagaki and artist Yusuke Murata, ***Eyeshield 21*** was originally serialized in Japan's ***Weekly Shonen Jump***. An OAV created for Shueisha's Anime Tour is available in Japan, and the ***Eyeshield 21*** hit animated TV series debuted in spring 2005!

ICHIRO TAKAMI

MAKOTO OTAWARA

DAIGO IKARI

GUNPEI SHOJI

KENGO MIZUMACHI

SHUN KAKEI

★The stories, characters and incidents mentioned in this publication are entirely fictional.

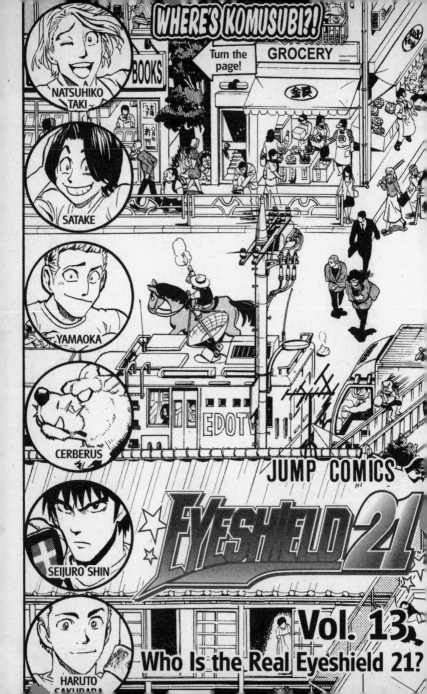

WHERE'S KOMUSUBI?

RUNAWAY

The streets of Deimon are crowded with faces you might have seen before. Can you find Komusubi among them? Speaking of which, one character was drawn twice! Whoever could it be? The answer is on page 116!

KAZUKI JUMONJI

KOJI KUROKI

SHOZO TOGANO

MARUTO

MANABU YUKIMITSU

DOBUROKU SAKAKI

TETSUO ISHIMARU

BULLETIN BOARD

Shy Sena Kobayakawa decides to reinvent himself during his first year at Deimon High by becoming the manager of the school football team. But when Sena's exceptional running ability comes to light, team captain Hiruma pressures him into playing under a secret identity, "Eyeshield 21." Sena's desire for victory has grown through competing with the Ojo White Knights, the Taiyo Sphinx and the NASA Aliens, and meeting talented rivals like Shin and Panther. The goal now is to make it to the Christmas Bowl! With this lofty ambition before them, the Devil Bats complete their so-called death march in America and move on to the Fall Tournament, taking on the Amino Cyborgs. Sena and his friends show the fruits of their training and win admirably over Amino, dispelling rumors that their opponent has the edge. On a winning streak, the Devil Bats beat the Yuhi Guts in the second round. Then the perennial powerhouse, the Hashiratani Deer, lose to the Kyoshin Poseidons and the tournament begins to get interesting...

The Story So Far

THE PLAYERS

SENA KOBAYAKAWA

YOICHI HIRUMA

RYOKAN KURITA

TARO RAIMON

MAMORI ANEZAKI

SUZUNA TAKI

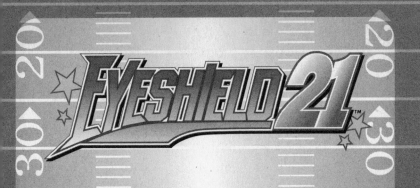

Vol. 13
Who Is the Real Eyeshield 21?

CONTENTS

Chapter 107 Who Is the Real Eyeshield 21?

...A FOOTBALL PLAYER'S PHYSIQUE BUT...

HUH HUF HUF

I WAS NEVER BLESSED WITH...

...RELYING ON TECHNIQUE ALONE.

...I'VE SENT LINEMEN TWICE MY SIZE FLYING...

OR YOU'LL FEEL THE BRUNT OF TEN YEARS OF ONIHEI'S...

...BLOOD AND SWEAT!!

SO DON'T MESS WITH ME, YOU SNOT-NOSED PUNK!

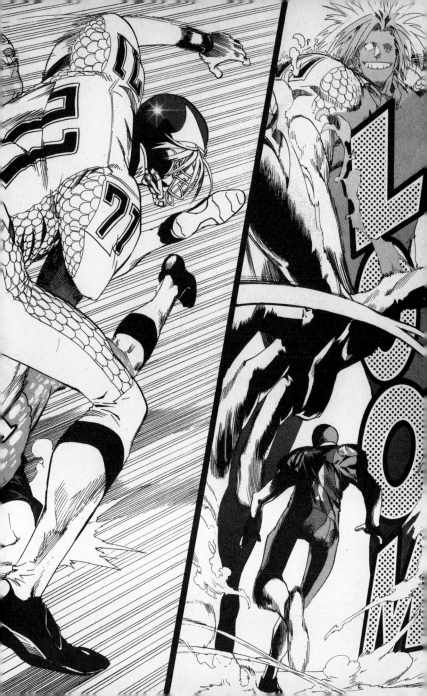

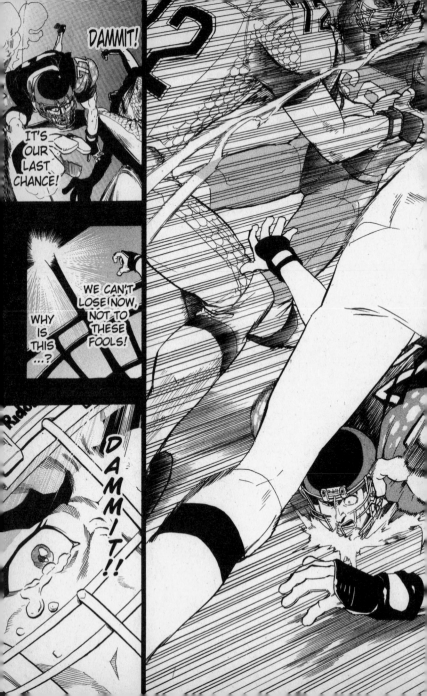

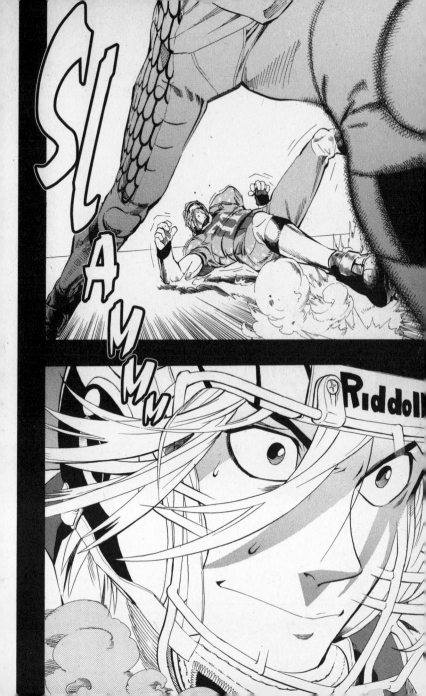

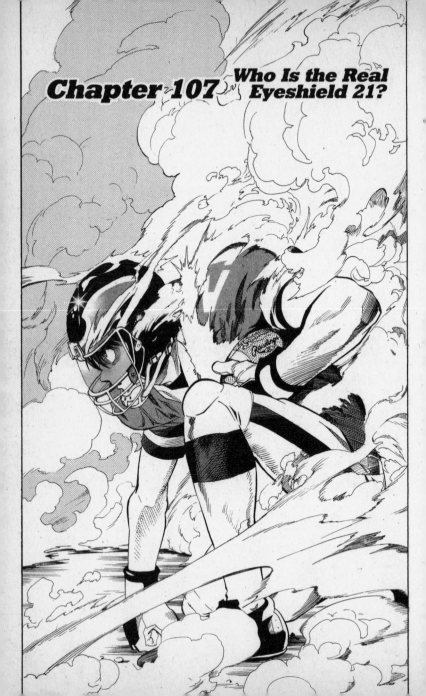

...ARE OUT AFTER THEIR FIRST MATCH!!

DEER | POSEIDONS
14 | 31

...THE FAVORED HASHIRATANI DEER...

I-INCREDIBLE. LED BY THE LEGENDARY ONIHEI...

ONIHEI

THE KYOSHIN POSEIDONS...

I NEVER THOUGHT...

...ARE A TOTAL DARK HORSE!

SLUMP!

NO...

NOT ONIHEI... NO...

12

CRINGE

YOU'RE TOO OLD!!

YOUR TIME IS *OVER!*

TALL AND SLENDER IS THE WAVE OF THE FUTURE!!

USE YOUR HEAD A LITTLE!

WHAT DO YOU THINK?!

WHAT? DID I SAY SOMETHING WRONG?

EVEN YOUR NAME IS, LIKE, ANCIENT!!

KNOW WHAT I'M SAYIN'?

HEY!

HEY!!

BACK OFF, MIZUMACHI!

SERIOUSLY?

...FOR THE GREAT ONIHEI?

IS THAT IT...

ROUND TWO

OTHER GAME RESULTS ...

IF YOU LOSE, YOU'RE OUT.

THAT'S RIGHT... THIS IS A TOURNAMENT.

GAAAAARR!!

AAAAAAH!!

CRUNCH

ROArr

OH NO, KOTARO!

THERE'RE ONLY 40 SECONDS LEFT!!

DAMN!!

TOUCH-DOWN!

URGYAAAH!

WE CAN'T LOSE NOW!

WE GOTTA GET BACK AT THOSE JERKS!!

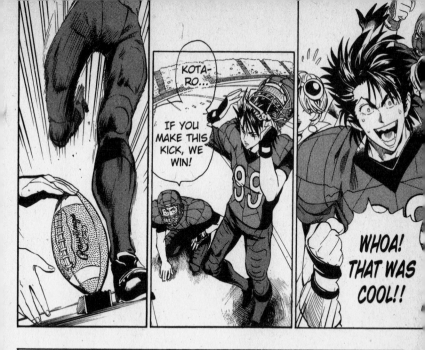

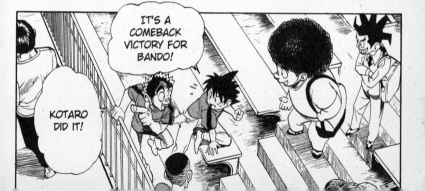

OH, DEPRAVED ENEMY, THOU WHO SEEKETH TO HARM THE NOROI OCCULTS...

...THE TEAM OF MY SON...

OH, JONANDAI GIANTS...

...MAY THOU BURNETH IN THE FIERY PIT OF HELL FOR ALL ETERNITY!

OOPS!

SLIP

CRUSH 'EM WITH YOUR SIZE! GO GIANTS!!

YOU *GIRLS* SHOULD BE OUT THERE!

GO GIANTS!

CURSE OF DEATH!

Jonandai Giants 0 — 6 Noroi Occults

TOUCH-DOWN!

SKIDDD

IT WORKED!

IT WAS A FLUKE...

MY CURSE WORKED!!

...ALWAYS KNOW OUR PLAYS?

HOW COME DOKU-BARI...

WOOOSH

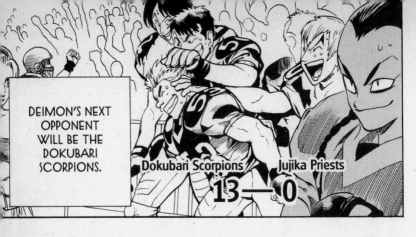
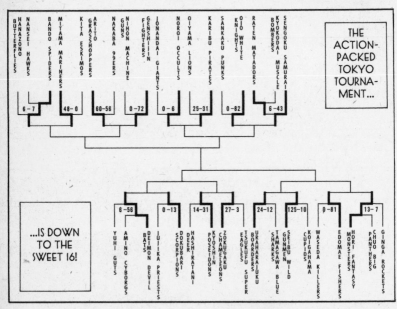
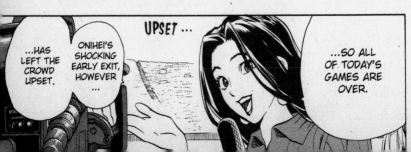

UPSET

...ABOUT THE POSEIDONS' SECRET?

HIRUMA, DID YOU KNOW...

A LITTLE.

...

I'M AMAZED THEY COULD TAKE DOWN HASHIRATANI LIKE THAT...

BUT THOSE GUYS NEVER PLAYED IN THE REGULAR SEASON...

...SO WE DON'T KNOW MUCH ABOUT THEM.

...EVERY-THING!!

...KICKOFFS, ONSIDE KICKS, RETURNS, PUNTS, PUNT RETURNS, TIGHT PUNTS...

OFFENSE, DEFENSE, TRY FOR POINT AND BLOCKS...

MAKE EDITED TAPES FOR EACH PLAYER, COVERING DIFFERENT SITUATIONS...

HEY, DAMN MANAGER!

TODAY'S VIDEO IS IMPORTANT.

CLIK CLIK CLIK CLIK

SHF SHF SHF

YESSIR!

SENA, YOU'D NEVER HAVE MADE IT AS MANAGER...

She got all that?

SHEESH!

GET ME NUMBERS...

PLAY CHOICE BY DOWN AND REMAINING YARDS...

20

TO ME, *HE'S* THE PAIN IN THE BUTT!

NOT FOR ME!

GOING UP AGAINST THEM WOULD BE A PAIN IN THE BUTT.

YEAH BUT KYOSHIN'S LINE IS HUGE...

...STOPPED EVEN ONIHEI COLD!!

THE SIZE DIFFER- ENCE...

EXCUSE ME! WE'D LIKE YOUR COMMENTS...

...ON THE PROMISING KYOSHIN POSEIDONS...

PUS

...HE'S AS HANDSOME AND SQUARE-JAWED AS A HOLLYWOOD MOVIE STAR!

ACCORDING TO CHEER-LEADER SUZUNA...

YOU'VE SAID TOO MUCH!

WHERE'S THE MAN BEHIND THE EYESHIELD?

...BUT... HUH?

YOU'VE SAID TOO MUCH, TOO!

OKAY, I'LL JUST WAIT UNTIL HE COMES BACK!

USE THE TOILET!!

Nice one!

...ALREADY LEFT TO--

W-WELL... EYE-SHIELD... UH...

ACKK! NOW I HAVE TO CHANGE AGAIN!

YEAH...

YOU GUYS COULD AT LEAST CHANGE OUT OF SIGHT!

MIZU-MACHI... WHERE ARE YOUR CLOTHES?

TEE HEE

TEE HEE

SHUFFLE SHUFFLE

OW!

SPROING

DONE!

Y-YES
...

HIYA
...

ARE YOU EYE-SHIELD...

HE'S... HUGE!!

BUT WHY IS HE ONLY IN BOXERS?

...21?!

HOPE WE MEET IN THE CHAMPION-SHIP! GLAD WE MET!

SHAKE SHAKE SHAKE

HAHAHAHAHA

YO, DUDE!

LIKE, WOW! WHAT LUCK!

THE BRACKETS AREN'T SET UP THAT WAY, DIMWIT!

IT'S THIS GUY, RIGHT? THE EXCHANGE STUDENT YOU MET IN AMERICA!

I JUST BUMPED INTO EYESHIELD!!

HEY, KAKEI!

WOOSH WOOSH

. . .

OH! YOU MEAN *THAT*!

WEREN'T YOU, LIKE, AN AWESOME EXCHANGE STUDENT AT NOTRE DAME?

EXCHANGE STUDENT?

AMERICA?

WE'VE GOT A TWO-SHOT OF EYESHIELD AND THE POSEIDONS!

HEY, LOOK!

I SAW WITH MY OWN EYES...

...THE BRILLIANT JAPANESE ATHLETE AT NOTRE DAME'S JUNIOR HIGH FEEDER SCHOOL.

THAT WAS TWO YEARS AGO.

WHEN I WAS IN JUNIOR HIGH...

...I WAS AN EXCHANGE STUDENT IN AMERICA.

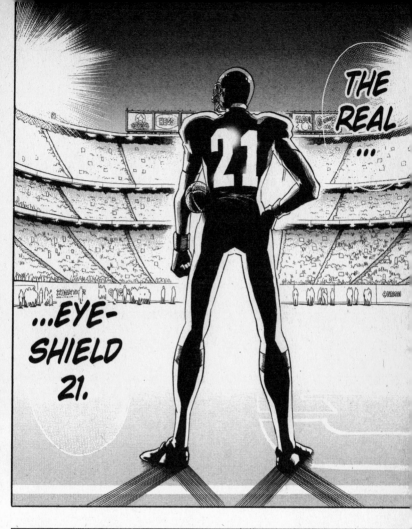

THE REAL...

...EYE-SHIELD 21.

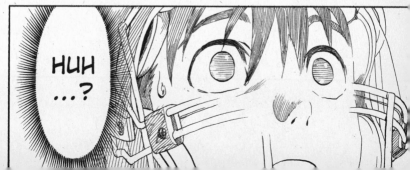

HUH...?

DID HE SAY THE *REAL*...

...EYE-SHIELD 21?

I'LL NEVER FORGET HIM.

HE WASN'T SHORT LIKE YOU.

YOUR CODE NAME IS...

...EYE-SHIELD 21!

...MADE UP OFF THE TOP OF HIS HEAD?!

THEN IT'S NOT JUST A NAME THAT HIRUMA...

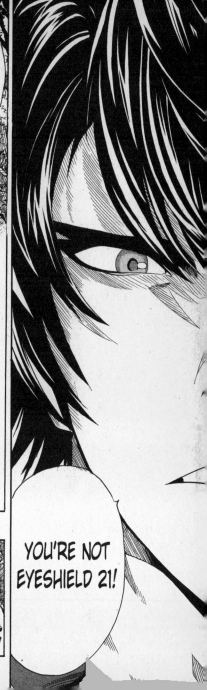

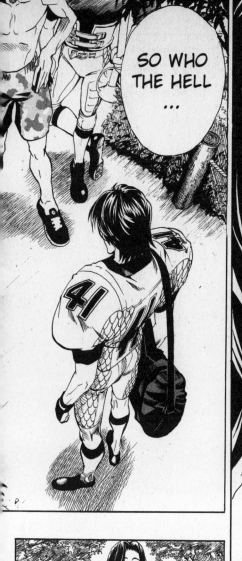

SO WHO
THE HELL
...

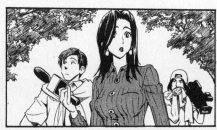

YOU'RE NOT
EYESHIELD 21!

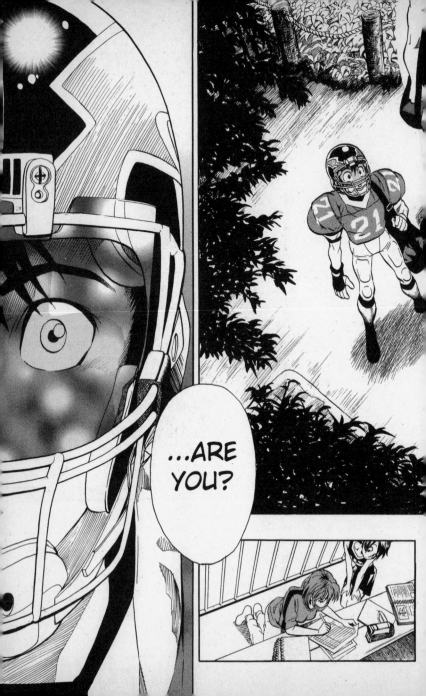

NOROI HIGH SCHOOL

Student Body: 481

Special Campus Facilities: Magic Circle

Major Career Options after Graduation

UNIVERSITY	EMPLOY-MENT	SHAMANISM

The school's special Hoodoo curriculum accounts for half of all classes. Of course, this puts a strain on the other subjects, but as the students like to say, "Hex your teacher, and you can get any grade you want!"

Graduate Testimonial

Head Nurse Oka

Know how I rose to be head nurse so quickly? I bet you thought **I put a curse on the hospital director!** Well, you're wrong! **I put a curse on myself,** one that would kill me if I didn't move up! That's the kind of spirit I learned at this school!

UNIFORM

...WAS A REAL PERSON AT AN AMERICAN SCHOOL?

EYESHIELD 21...

Chapter 108 The Real Body

HE WAS CALLED EYESHIELD 21.

HE WAS A JAPANESE EXCHANGE STUDENT...

...WHO WAS A SUPERB RUNNER.

OF COURSE, THIS WAS BACK IN JUNIOR HIGH.

...AND MOST OF ALL...

...HE COULDN'T BE STOPPED.

WITH HIS HEIGHT AND POWER...

...HE NEVER LOST TO THE AMERICAN GUYS.

TOP-CLASS SPEED...

...TECHNI-QUE...

...BALANCE...

°°°

...I MEAN, I DIDN'T KNOW THAT, UH...

THAT'S...

THEN ARE YOU...

...A FAKE?!

EYE-SHIELD'S TALL?

RIGHT, EYESHIELD 21?

HEH HEH HEH! HE SHRANK!

ENOUGH, MIZUMACHI!

THE TRUTH WILL BE REVEALED IN THE GAME.

NO WAY, MAN! DIDN'T HAPPEN! NOT ONCE!

HAPPENS ALL THE TIME, DOESN'T IT?

ONE MORNING YOU WAKE UP AND YOU REALIZE YOU'VE SHRUNK BY A FOOT!

WITH YOUR DELICATE BUILD AND SMALL SIZE...

WHAT WAS THAT?

WHAT WERE YOU TALKING ABOUT?

...YOU'LL NEVER BE IN THE SAME LEAGUE AS THE REAL EYESHIELD.

Chapter 108 The Real Body

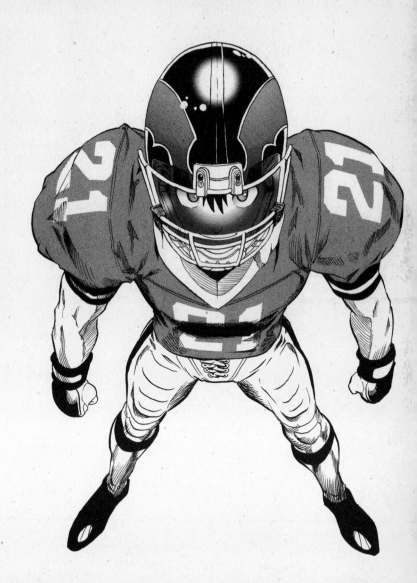

--TY!!

PAR--

YAKINIKU

GRILLED MEAT

MINOTAUR

SIZZLE--!!

TASTY!!

WHOOEE! SMELLS GREAT!

CONGRATS ON SURVIVING THE SECOND ROUND!!

NOT ENOUGH DAMN FIREPOWER!

YOU'RE MISSING THE MEAT!

I'M NOT MUCH OF SPEAKER BUT I'LL TRY TO LIVE UP TO YOUR...

THANK YOU, EVERY-ONE...

...FOR THIS YAKINIKU PARTY TO CELEBRATE MY SHINING DEBUT MATCH!

• • •

A BLUFF WON'T WORK WITHOUT ANY TRUTH BEHIND IT!

OF COURSE!

...ABOUT THE REAL EYESHIELD 21?

HIRUMA, DID YOU KNOW...

...YOU'LL NEVER BE IN THE SAME LEAGUE AS THE REAL EYESHIELD.

WITH YOUR DELICATE BUILD AND SMALL SIZE ...

...BUT HE'S MUCH TALLER THAN ME.

I MEAN, IS THERE ANY PLAYER SHORTER THAN ME?

SHIN...

...IS NOT THAT TALL...

EVEN THE MASTERFUL ONIHEI...

...WAS CRUSHED BY THEIR HEIGHT.

UNH?

WHAT? SOMETHING WRONG?

IT'S DEIMON!!

IT'S THE REAL SHIN!!

EVEN AFTER 30 YEARS...

...WE STILL THINK ALIKE. WE NEVER GREW UP!

YAKINIKU AFTER THE GAME! DAMN STRAIGHT!

GA HA HA!

DOBU...

WOULDN'T YOU SAY SO...

...SHOJI?

...ROKU!!!

THOSE TWO...

WHAT'S THEIR CONNECTION?

THEY WERE CALLED THE TWO SWORDS.

THEY WERE THE ACE COMBO OF SENGOKU UNIVERSITY.

JUST AS YOU SAY...

A LOT HAS HAPPENED.

YUP.

I KNEW I'D BE YOUR OPPONENT...

...AND MADE MYSELF DEIMON'S TRAINER.

A LOT HAS HAPPENED.

I HATE MYSELF FOR EVER THINKING HE WAS COOL!

...IS DEEP IN HIS HARDBOILED WORLD!

DOBUROKU! THAT DRUNKEN OLD LECHER...

GRRRRR

HEY! BRING ME 30 MORE!!

YIKES! KURITA IS ONTO HIS TWENTIETH PLATE!!

MUNCH MUNCH

BAH!

FRED

WHEN IT COMES TO COOL, NO ONE CAN OUT-COOL OUR COACH!

UM...

...TOUGH TO JOIN...

THAT TABLE IS A LITTLE...

WHAT'S WITH THE ANTENNA?

...MAMORI'S GOT SOMETHING GOING ON.

CHATTER

MAYBE NOT YOU, BUT I THINK...

CHITTER

I'M NOT DATING ANY OF THE PLAYERS!

THIS ONE'S EVEN TOUGHER...

NO, REALLY! I'M NOT!

ACKK! THIS TABLE IS DEFINITELY OUT OF THE QUESTION!

...ISN'T IT JUST AN ANCIENT EUROPEAN WEAPON?

BATTLE OF SNOOPS

UH...

BATTLE OF THE BRAINS

SO THE BALLISTA...

...IS OJO'S NEW DEFENSIVE STRATEGY. AM I RIGHT?

CHOMP CHOMP

QUIT SCREWING AROUND AND EAT!!

AND SOMEHOW WE GOT STUCK ON THIS BATTLEFIELD...

WHERE THE HELL HAVE YOU BEEN?!

THE LOSER FOOTS THE BILL!!

I'LL TAKE THE CHALLENGE!!

HUUUUHHHH?!

GATHUNK

THE FIRST TEAM TO FINISH WINS!!

EACH TEAM GETS FIVE HUNDRED SLICES OF KALBI!!※

※ THINLY SLICED BEEF FROM SHORT RIBS, MARINATED AND GRILLED KOREAN STYLE.

CLINK...

FOUR HUNDRED AND...

...TWENTY-FIVE!

GASHUNK

CHOMP CHOMP

MINOTAU

All right!

I'm going into battle mode!

CHOMP CHOMP

GASH-UNK

BLECH!

NO MORE...

HUH?

...I'LL BE ABLE TO EAT SOME MORE...

TEETER...

MAYBE IF I REST OUTSIDE...

WELCOME

ONE...

TWO...

ONE...

WHA—!?!!

THIS IS WEIRD, ANY WAY YOU LOOK AT IT...

EATING WELL IS CRUCIAL...

...FOR DEVELOPING A REAL ATHLETE'S BODY.

"INGESTED"...?

IT'S NOT THAT I DON'T EAT...

I'VE ALREADY INGESTED THE NECESSARY AMOUNT.

°°°

A REAL...

...WHO'S HARDER TO STOP...

...A TALL, WELL-BUILT RUNNER...

...OR A PIPSQUEAK LIKE ME?

SHIN, WHEN YOU'RE PLAYING DEFENSE...

YOU MEAN, ALL THINGS BEING EQUAL... INCLUDING SPEED AND AGILITY?

I JUST WONDERED, THAT'S ALL!!

UH, I DON'T MEAN ANYTHING BY IT!

•••

I THOUGHT SO.

MAKES SENSE.

I THOUGHT SO.

•••

YEAH...

THE TALL, WELL-BUILT ONE.

HE WON'T BE STOPPED BY JUST ANY TACKLE.

IF YOU'RE TORMENTED BY FEELINGS OF INFERIORITY BEFORE YOU FIGHT...

...DEIMON WON'T STAND A CHANCE.

THE TRUMP CARD IS UNFLINCHING INNER STRENGTH.

THE STRENGTH OF A HIT...

...DOESN'T DEPEND SOLELY ON PHYSIQUE.

...TO GET THE TEAM TO THE CHRISTMAS BOWL!

I WANT TO KNOW MY WEAK POINTS EARLY ON...

...SO I CAN DO WHATEVER I NEED...

IT'S NOT ABOUT FEELING INFERIOR.

WELCOME

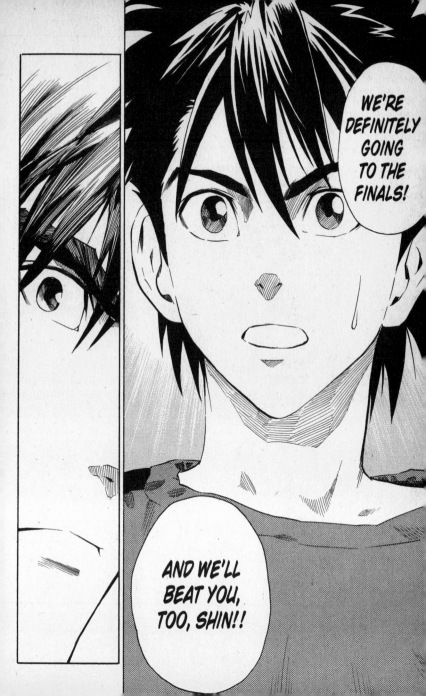

IT'S JUST LIKE AT THE TRYOUTS.

ONCE IN A WHILE...

...HE MANAGES TO SAY THE COOLEST THINGS.

IT'S ESPECIALLY IMPORTANT FOR A BODY LIKE YOURS THAT'S STILL DEVELOPING.

YAKINIKU'S NOT A BAD SOURCE.

...WON'T CHANGE, EVEN IF YOU TELL IT TO.

YOUR HEIGHT...

...THEN AFTER TRAINING OR A GAME LIKE TODAY'S...

...YOU SHOULD GET SOME PROTEIN.

IF YOU'RE WORRIED ABOUT YOUR BODY...

WHEEEN

CLOMP!!

SO THE LOSER PAYS...

LET'S SEE... EACH TEAM ATE 500 DISHES...

WE HAVE TO WIN, EVEN IF IT K-KILLS US...

1200
600
1300
2200
700
+
¥58万1200

ABOUT U.S. $5,000

SO CLOSE AND YET...

DAMN...

SIZZLE

48

CHOMP CHOMP CHOMP

WHOA!!

DA-DUM

ABOUT 500 YEN?

HOW MUCH WAS THE TAB?

WE WIN!

YEAH!!

NO, IT'S NOT!!

GOOD...

GUESS IT WAS ALL YOU CAN EAT!

AUTUMN
ALL-YOU-CAN-EAT
SPECIAL
YAKINIKU

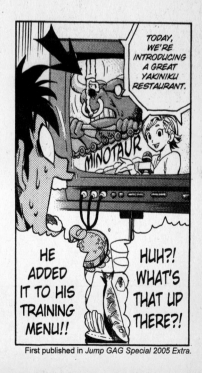

First published in *Jump GAG Special 2005 Extra*.

PRIMP

Chapter 109: STING

...IT WAS A MESSAGE FROM HIRUMA.

BUT KURITA SAID...

WHAT?

HMM, WONDER WHAT IT'S FOR...?

BABOING!

I SAID TO BRING LIPSTICK TO THE GAME TODAY...

...NOT *WEAR* IT!

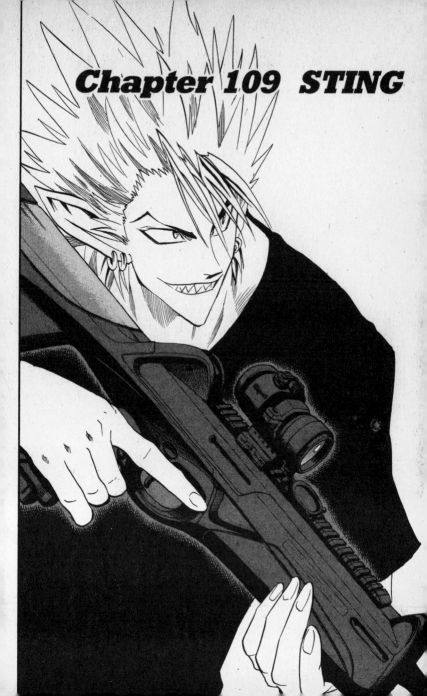

SEPTEMBER 25

ROUND THREE OF THE NATIONAL HIGH SCHOOL FOOTBALL CHAMPIONSHIP...

WHAT'S WITH DEIMON AND ALL THE MAKE-UP?

I DON'T KNOW BUT...

...THEY LOOK PRETTY PUMPED.

HEH HEH HEH

...DOKUBARI, OVER THERE.

THEIR OPPONENT IS...

VWOOSH

VWOOSH

ONE LOSS?!

TEN WINS...

THE DOKUBARI SCORPIONS'...

...RECORD THIS YEAR IS...

FWOOOOM

EVEN SO, OJO AND SEIBU...

...ARE NO MATCH FOR US!

Dokubari Scorpions

Captain Kanagushi

THEY DIDN'T FACE STIFF COMPETITION LIKE OJO OR SEIBU, THOUGH.

S-STILL, THAT'S AMAZING!

SHEE HEE HEE HEE!

SO THIS IS THE FIRST ROUND VIDEO...

...OF THE DOKUBARI SCORPIONS.

THEY'RE READING THE OTHER TEAM'S PLAYS LEFT AND RIGHT.

THAT'S HOW THEY WIN.

SP 3.47min ▶PLAY

POLYCRYSTALLINE SILICON

...HAS A PIPELINE TO THEIR OPPONENT'S PLANS.

IT'S AS IF SOMEHOW DOKU-BARI...

IT'S FOOT-BALL WE'RE PLAYING HERE!

A BATTLE OF THE MINDS!

SHEE HEE HEE! THAT'S RIGHT.

TRUE TO OUR NAME...

...ARE WASTING THEIR TIME.

THOSE MEAT-HEADS...

POOR DEIMON! THEY'RE TRYING SO HARD!

DOOM

...WE'VE GOT YOU ALL...

...UNDER THE SCORPION'S STINGER!!

ROOOAAR

SET!!

DID YOU SAY...

...JUST BY ANALYZING THE REGULAR SEASON DATA.

THEY AREN'T GUESSING THEIR OPPONENT'S STRATEGIES THIS WELL...

..."HABITS"?

YEAH.

WHEN A...

...QUARTERBACK'S GOING TO PASS...

...HE LICKS HIS FINGERS FOR A BETTER GRIP.

FWOOM...

THAT GUY, KANAGUSHI...

...IS WATCHING DEIMON'S TINIEST HABITS!

BLONDIE THERE DIDN'T LICK HIS FINGERS...

...SO HE WON'T PASS.

•••

KRIK

...BEFORE THEY CHARGE.

...THEY'LL LEAN FORWARD...

IF THEY PLAN FOR A RUN, INSTEAD OF A PASS...

WATCH THE FINGERS ON THE GROUND!

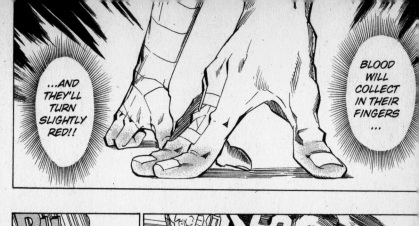

...AND THEY'LL TURN SLIGHTLY RED!!

BLOOD WILL COLLECT IN THEIR FINGERS...

RUMBLE

HO-HO! THEY'RE COMING FULL ON!

77

RUMBLE

STOP THE RUN!!!

SHEE HEE HEE! THERE THEY GO!

DEIMON'S GONNA RUN!!

TOSS

THIS GAME IS PATHETIC!!

STICK

RUB RUB

NO WAY... THEIR FINGERS...

...CLEARLY TURNED RED!

KSHEEEE!!

WHAT?! A PASS TO THE MONKEY?!

...ON THAT COUNT.

YOU'D BE CRAZY TO COMPETE WITH HIRUMA...

DEIMON IS TOO DEVIOUS.

THE PLAYER WHO'S GONNA CATCH THE BALL...

...WILL BE ABNORMALLY KEYED UP WHEN HE TAKES HIS POSITION!

READ THE PASS RECEIVER!

...I'LL GET IT RIGHT!

THIS TIME...

THAT LOOKS ABNORMAL!!

THE BALL'S GOING TO HIM!

SHWOOP

AH HA HA!!

TOSS

HE FAKES *HIMSELF* OUT!

WIRLL

?

IMPOSSIBLE ...!!

WAS THAT WEIRDNESS ALL A FAKE?

KSHEEEE!!!

WHAT?! A PASS TO THE MONKEY?!!

RAAH...

WATCH THE RECEIVER'S EYES.

IF HE STARTS LOOKING AROUND...

HE ONLY DOES IT...

...TO HIDE WHERE HE LOOKED FIRST.

HE ALREADY KNOWS HIS ROUTE, SO HE DOESN'T NEED TO LOOK AROUND.

THE FIRST?

NOT THE LAST?

...REMEMBER WHERE HE LOOKED FIRST.

THAT'S WHERE HE'LL MAKE HIS CUT.

ooo!!

GLANCE GLANCE

SLAP

IT'S TRUE...

SHOOM

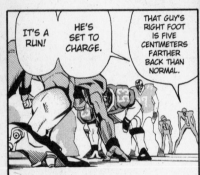

IT'S A RUN!

HE'S SET TO CHARGE.

THAT GUY'S RIGHT FOOT IS FIVE CENTIMETERS FARTHER BACK THAN NORMAL.

DEI- MON!!

DEI- MON!!

CRUMMP

WOW! THEY BLOCKED THE RUN AGAIN!!

NO MORE PLAY READING!!

KSHAAAAW!!

HEH HEH HEH. A CHEAP TRICK LIKE THAT...

...ONLY WORKS ON SCUM TEAMS THAT HAVEN'T GOTTEN RID OF THEIR BAD HABITS.

BUT THEY HAD NO IDEA THEIR PLAYS COULD BE READ, TOO.

THOSE DOKUBARI GUYS...

...GOT THIS FAR WITH THEIR PATHETIC READING OF OUR PLAYS.

GULP

DEIMON HAS FEWER PLAYERS.

BUT DOKUBARI STILL WINS WITH ITS BRAINS!

CRUSH THEM AND WEAR OUT THEIR STAMINA!!

RUMBLE

HRRNGH!!

BAM

WHAM

SQUASH THE LITTLE GUY!!

UMPH!!

PUSH PUSH PUSH PUSH

RRR GRRRRR !!!

PUSH!

THE STRENGTH OF A HIT...

...DOESN'T DEPEND SOLELY ON PHYSIQUE.

YOU'LL NEVER BE IN THE SAME LEAGUE...

...AS THE REAL EYESHIELD.

THUMP

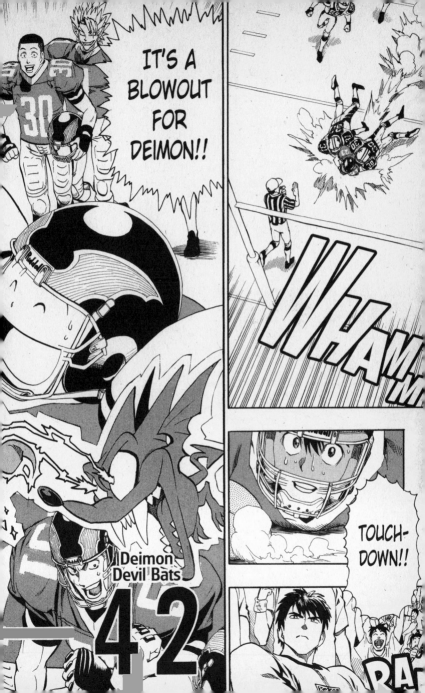

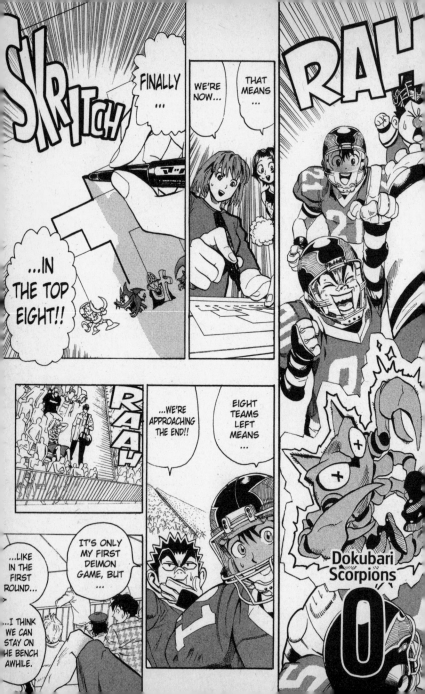

THEY'RE NO MATCH FOR US...

...RIGHT, KAKEI?

LET'S TAKE 'EM TO THE CLEANERS!

ALL RIGHT!

FIRST, ZOKU-GAKU.

STARTING TODAY...

...WE'RE IN FROM THE START!

THERE'S NO NEED TO HIDE ANYMORE.

BUDABUDABUDABUDA

WE'RE A DIFFERENT TEAM THAN IN THE SPRING.

YEAH, 'CAUSE WE WENT THROUGH HELL IN SUMMER TRAINING...

"THE CLEANERS"...

...HUH?!

KEGH!!

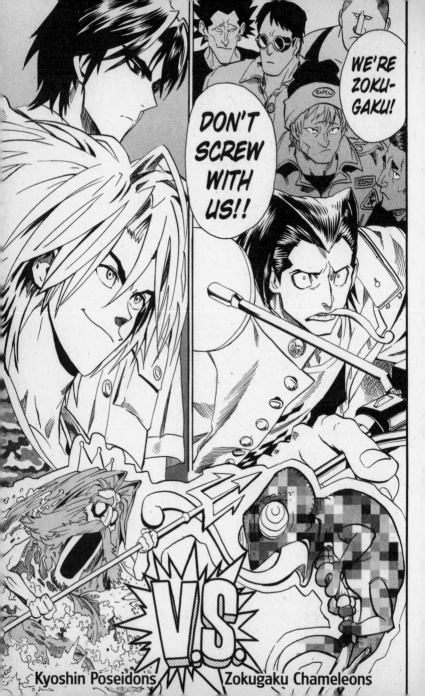

Kyoshin Poseidons   Zokugaku Chameleons

High School Selection Guidance for Prospective Applicants!

ZOKUGAKU ACADEMY

Student Body: 1,240

Special Campus Facilities: Gas Station

Major Career Options after Graduation

UNIVERSITY	CYCLE SHOP	COURIER	OTHER

CIRCUS RIDING

Whether you're in class or on a break, someone's always taking aim at the back of your skull with a baseball bat! Recommended for those seeking a survivalist lifestyle in high school!

Graduate Testimonial

MEG TSUYUMINE

Join the football club, or I'll crush your balls!

UNIFORM

Chapter 110 Ruled by Fear

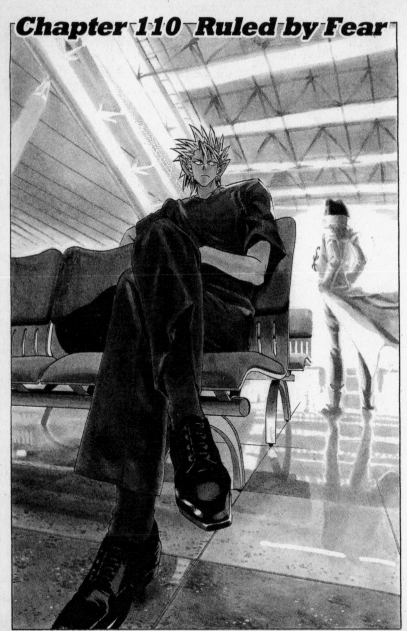

ROOOAR

WHOA! IT'S THE ABSOLUTE BADDEST...

RUI HABA-SHIRA!

STARE

R

GO FOR IT, ZOKU-GAKU!!

UMM...

HUH?

VROOM

OH, THAT'S RIGHT. WE OWE HIM FOR GIVING YOU A LIFT!!

...SO SHOW US YOU'RE A MAN!!

YOU'RE TOKAGE HABA-SHIRA'S LITTLE BROTHER...

ZOKU-GAKU CHAME-LEONS!!

LISTEN UP, SCUMBAGS !!

KEGH !!

CHUNK

IT'S HABASHIRA'S...

...LAST SHOT AT THE CHRISTMAS BOWL, TOO!

FLAP

THIS IS ZOKUGAKU'S LAST FALL TOURNAMENT!

AND THERE WON'T BE A NEXT TIME FOR YOU, EITHER!

YOU SCUMBAGS WANT REVENGE, DON'T YOU?!

IF WE BEAT KYOSHIN, OUR FATED CLASH WITH DEIMON IS NEXT!

DA-DUM-DUM!

WHOA!

RORAAR

HERE COME THE KYOSHIN POSEI-DONS!

DA-DUM!

THEY **ARE** BIG!!

BIGGER THAN ZOKUGAKU BY FAR...

KEGH!

CHANGING COLOR TO MATCH YOUR OPPONENT, THAT'S CHAMELEON POWER!

SNIK!

MURMUR MURMUR!

WAS ZOKU-GAKU'S LINE...

...THAT TALL BEFORE?!

THEY SET UP A BIG LINE TO COUNTER OURS.

HISSSSSS

Hebii, Zokugaku lineman

Height: 184 cm (6'1") / Weight: 120 kg (265 lb.)

THIS IS GONNA BE FUN!!

UH-HUH!

SET!

WOW! IT'S A CLASH OF THE TITANS!

THIS'LL BE SPECTA-CULAR!!

ROOAR

MURMUR

WHAT'S WITH HIS POSTURE?

STREETCH...

IS HE STUPID?

HUH?

MIZU-MACHI...

YEP...

I'M USED TO MY WAY!

YOU REALLY THINK THAT'LL MAKE YOU FASTER?

DI VE

...KENGO MIZUMACHI!!

SE

JOLT!!

HE WAS THE TALK OF THE SWIM CLUB TWO YEARS AGO...

I GET IT NOW!

...BLAZING LIKE A COMET AT THE JUNIOR HIGH SWIM MEET...

IT'S SWIMMING LEGEND...

...AND THEN VANISHING ALL OF A SUDDEN.

HISSSSS!

IN LANE THREE... IT'S MIZUMACHI!

FOR THE 50-METER FREESTYLE...

WAH HA HA HA! THAT'S IT, GUYS! KICK THEIR BUTTS!

WHOA! THAT'S SOME HEAVY-WEIGHT BLOCK!

!!

DAMN! THAT GUY'S ARM--!!

HEBII, YOU SCUMBAG!

...IT'LL BE THE CRAWL, NATURALLY!

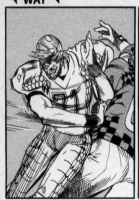
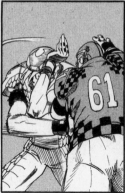
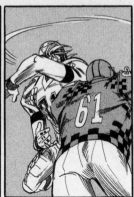

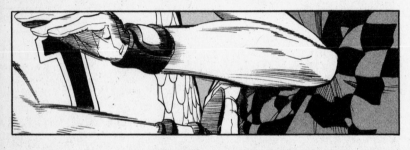

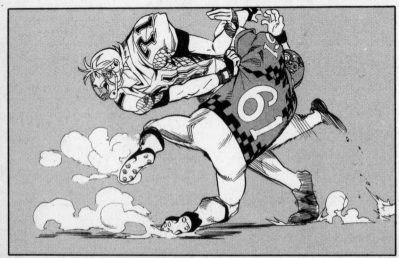

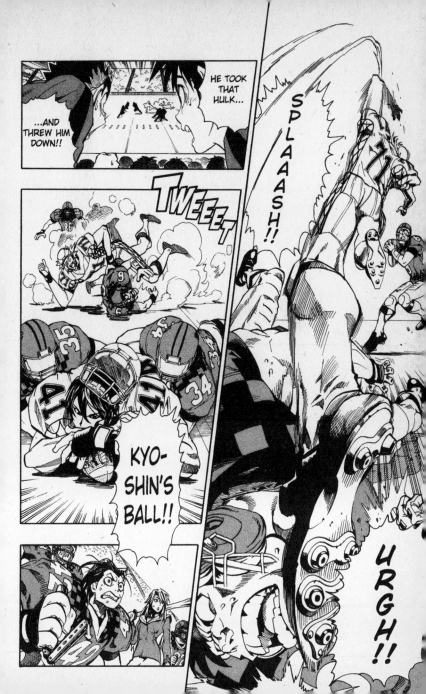

...AND DO THE KILLER LINEMAN TECHNIQUE...

HIS HEIGHT GIVES HIM THE EDGE...

...TO REACH OVER...

...AND PUSHES OFF THE GUY WITH HIS OTHER HAND.

HE REACHES OVER HIS OPPONENT'S HEAD, LIKE HE'S DOING THE CRAWL...

...KNOWN AS "THE SWIM"!!

STOP THE NEXT PLAY, THAT'S ALL!

DEFENSE, WE'RE ON!!

CLOMP

YOU IDIOT! THE GAME JUST STARTED.

KEGH! WHAT ARE YOU SAYING?

IF HEBII OF ALL PEOPLE COULDN'T STOP HIM...

LIKE I SAID...

...WE CHANGE TO MATCH OUR OPPONENT. THAT'S CHAMELEON POWER!

THIS TIME ZOKU-GAKU'S COMING OUT WITH A *SHORT* LINEUP!

WHAT'S THIS?

VWOOOOSH!

KEEE EEGH!

RUI HABASHIRA BREAKS THROUGH!!

DURING SUMMER VACATION...

...ZOKU-GAKU WASN'T JUST SCREWING AROUND!

WOW, HE'S FAST!!

A LOT FASTER THAN WHEN WE FACED THEM!

...OUR DEFENSE WILL USE SPEED TO THROW 'EM OFF.

IF SIZE DOESN'T WORK...

GOTCHA!!

UMF!!

GO, CHAMELEONS!!

...then speed will.

If size doesn't work...

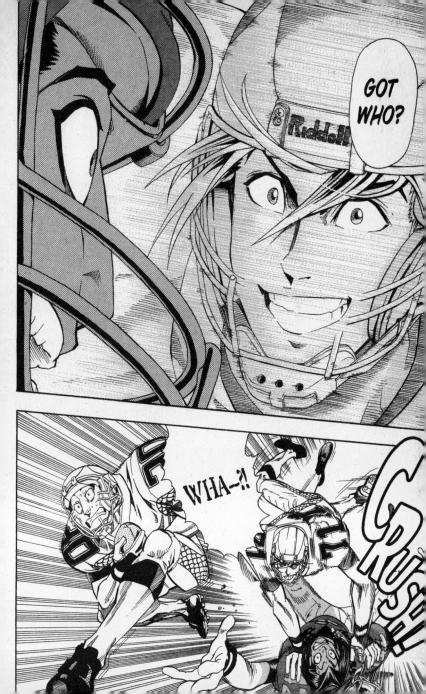

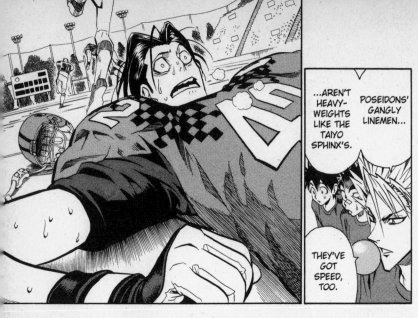
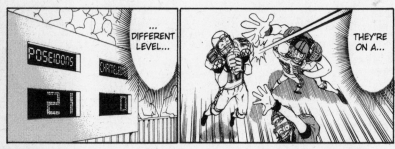
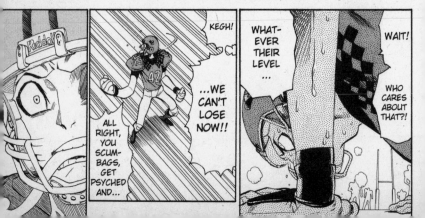

WHAT ARE YOU TALKING ABOUT, YOU IDIOT?!

IT AIN'T OVER TILL IT'S OVER! FOOLS!!

NAH... WE'RE GONERS.

THEY GOT US ON SIZE *AND* SKILL...

REMEMBER HOW HARD WE TRAINED THIS SUMMER!

DON'T LET 'EM WALK ALL OVER US!

I TOLD YOU BEFORE THE GAME--

THIS IS OUR LAST CHANCE AT THE CHRISTMAS BOWL!!

YOU WANT ME TO **KILL** YOU?

SAY I'M RIGHT!

IF WE DON'T COME UP WITH A PLAN...

WE FACE KYOSHIN NEXT.

THAT COULD BE US.

POSEIDONS 42

CHAMELEONS 0

...LOST.

HABA-SHIRA'S TEAM...

THAT'S THE END OF MY CHRISTMAS BOWL DREAM.

KEGH...

KERBONK

IN MY BIG BROTHER'S TIME...

...WITH NERVES OF STEEL!

...THERE WERE STILL A FEW ZOKUGAKU GUYS...

WHY'D YOU GIVE UP?

YOU WUSSIES!!!

...BUT EVERYONE EXCEPT YOU...

...GAVE UP MIDWAY.

YOU HAD A CHANCE OF WINNING...

KEGH!

THE ONLY WAY TO HOLD THIS LOT TOGETHER...

IT'S ALL, "THAT SUCKS!" OR "I'M BORED!"

GUYS OUR AGE ARE DIFFERENT.

YOU'RE LIKE ME!

THAT'S HOW YOU'VE KEPT YOUR TEAM TOGETHER.

...IS BY SHEER FORCE!

ONE CAN ONLY RULE BY FEAR!

ARE YOU TELLING ME I GOT IT WRONG?

...DID MY TEAM FALL APART?

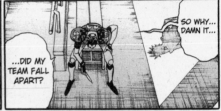

SO WHY... DAMN IT...

WHY ARE THEY SIDING WITH YOU...

...AND AIMING FOR THE CHRISTMAS BOWL?

HOW COME IT ISN'T FEAR...

...THAT MAKES YOUR GUYS WORK SO HARD?!

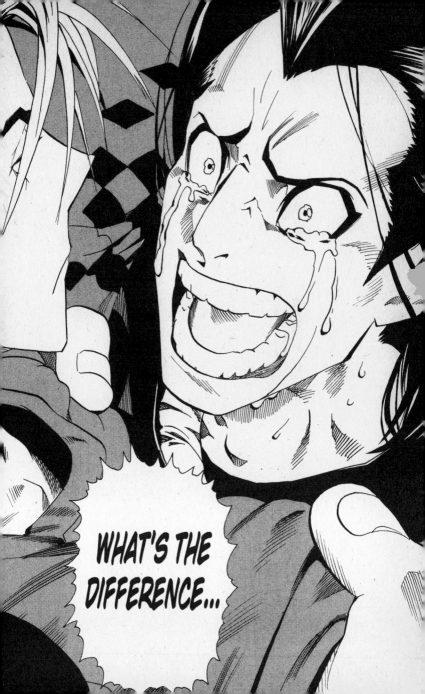

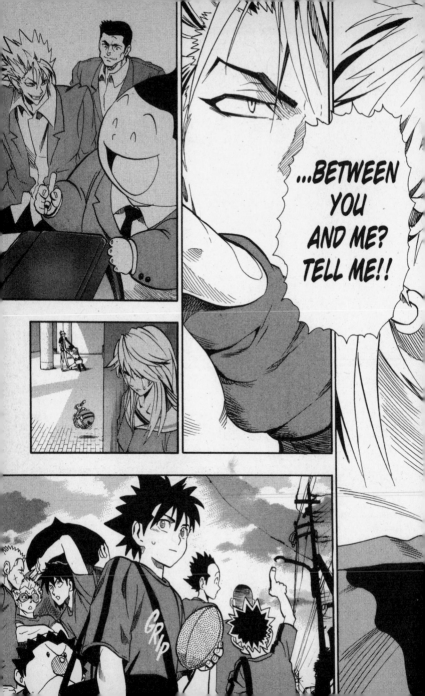

Investigation File #034

Uncover the secrets of flexibility!!

WHAT DO I HAVE TO DO TO BE FLEXIBLE, LIKE TAKI?

Caller

S.T., Osaka Prefecture

BELIEVE IN YOURSELF! YOU HAVE A 100 PERCENT CHANCE OF BEING FLEXIBLE!!

A FOOL'S ANSWER IS NO ANSWER AT ALL, SO I'LL HAVE TO EXPLAIN THE STRETCHING EXERCISES MYSELF!

Rule 2

Always exhale as you bend.

Rule 1

Always do them after your shower.

Rule 3

Oh, and never push too hard all at once!!

FOLLOW THESE THREE RULES AND STRETCH EVERY DAY!
BIT BY BIT, YOU'LL BECOME MORE FLEXIBLE!
TRUST ME!

Chapter 111 The Quarterfinals

WE'LL SLICE OJO INTO TINY PIECES!

THAT'S ONLY FITTING FROM THE COACH OF THE VENERABLE SENGOKU SAMURAI!!

FLAP FLAP

MASTER OF THE UNIVERSE

WA HA HA! GET MY GOOD SIDE!

WAP

HEY!!

Who's stubborn?!

EVEN AS THE CAPTAIN, HE WAS AN OBSESSIVE NUISANCE.

I'M GONNA TEACH HIM THAT FOOTBALL'S NOT ALL ABOUT DISCIPLINE AND...

HUNH?!

THAT STUBBORN COACH SHOJI AND I...

...WERE IN THE SENGOKUDAI FOOTBALL CLUB.

CLINK

CLANK

I WONDER IF IKARI WILL *EVER* GET TO DEBUT...

PUT A SOCK IN IT BACK THERE!! GEEZ!!

THEY SURE HAVE A GREAT OFFENSE.

HIS RUNNING'S SHARP!!

YOU CAN SEE WHY SENGOKU IS A FAVORITE!!

HO HA HA HA HA HA!!

ROOOARRR!!

FWOOOSH

FWOOOOOOM

WITH THAT, THE TOURNAMENT ARRIVES AT THE TOP EIGHT!

THE ONLY ONES LEFT...

...AS WE ENTER THE FINAL STAGES, ARE THE POWER-HOUSES!!

HwOoOoOo

...THIS YEAR'S OJO WHITE KNIGHTS...

...MAY BE A TEAM...

...TO EXCEED ALL EXPECTATIONS!

STRETCH-ER!

STRETCH-ERRRR!

I KNEW THEY WERE STRONG...

...BUT...

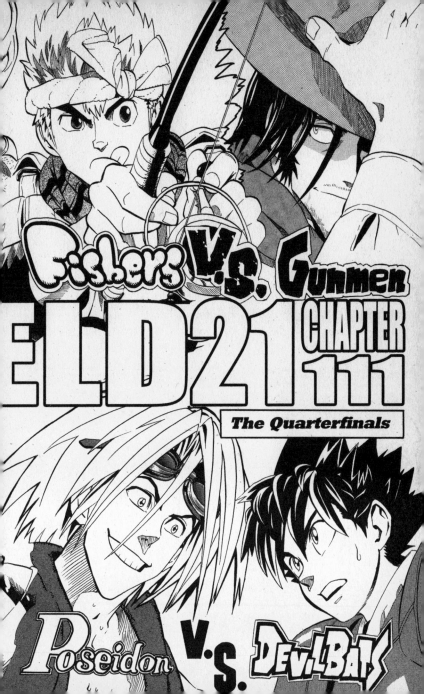

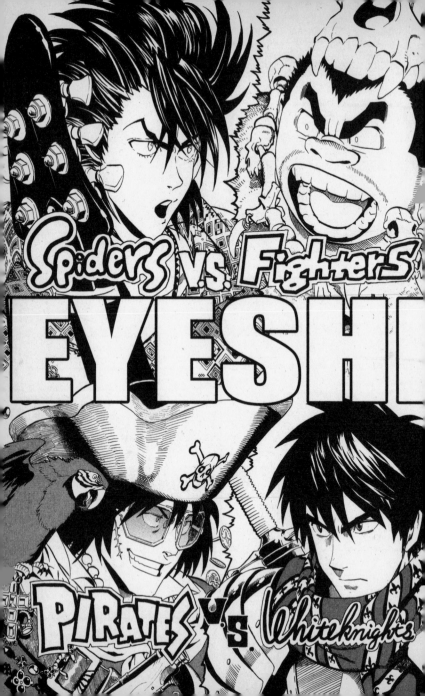

THWAK

THWAK

SNEAK SNEAK

WE WERE PASSING BY...

...AND SAW DEIMON TRAINING BY CHANCE!

NO, NO...

THIS ISN'T RIGHT.

I MEAN, WE'RE SPYING!

PE EK

Kyoshin Poseidons

Quarterback
Kobanzame

HUH?

ALL RIGHT!

BRING IT ON!!

DA-DUM

WHAT KIND OF TRAINING IS THAT?!

STILTS...?

YOU KNOW HOW KYOSHIN'S LINEMEN ARE ALL SO TALL?

WELL, OUR MOCK KYOSHIN LINEMAN CAN GET ON THESE.

IT'LL BE JUST LIKE THE REAL THING!

UH, I DON'T THINK SO...

TAK TAK TAK TAK TAK

GABLONK OW!!

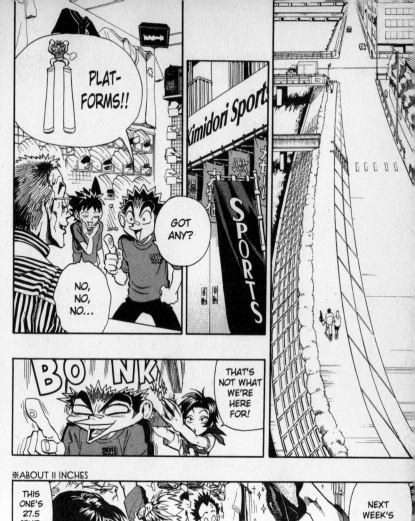

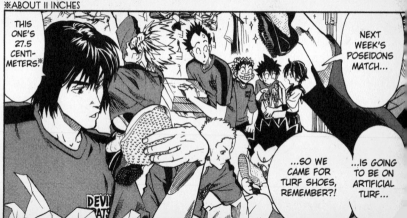

WHOA! IMPRESSIVE!

THWUMMP!

FORTY CENTIMETERS!!!※

※ABOUT 15 1/2 INCHES

24.0

I'VE HEARD THAT NAME BEFORE...

YOICHI?

BRING THE BOXES OF CLEATS FROM THE BACK.

YOICHI!

HEY, PART-TIMER!

A BIG SHIPMENT CAME IN TODAY.

WE HAVE EVEN BIGGER SIZES.

Kimidori Spor

YESSIR, MR. MANAGER!!

TURF SHOES

TURF SHOES

HUH?! WHAT'S *HE* DOING HERE?!!

KACHINC

HOW MAY I HELP YOU?

WHAT KIND OF SHOPKEEPER POINTS A GUN AT HIS CUSTOMERS?!

YIKES! I'D LIKE TO LEAVE NOW, PLEASE...

I STARTED PART-TIME HERE TODAY.

OH, DIDN'T I TELL YOU GUYS?

HUH?! YOU ARE?!

AND I'M QUITTING TODAY, TOO!

WHEEN

HERE! IT'S HERE!

THE SHOP-KEEPER'S A WIMP. IT'S SHOPLIFTER HEAVEN!

FOR REAL?!

SIR...

UH... YES, PLEASE.

SHALL I DELIVER THEM?

KYOSHIN HIGH SCHOOL ALSO BOUGHT CLEATS FOR ARTIFICIAL TURF.

BUT HIRUMA...

...WHY'D YOU TAKE A PART-TIME JOB?

CAN'T CALL *THAT* SPYING!

...AND HAPPENING TO PEEK IN ON KYOSHIN TRAINING...

DELIVERING PACKAGES PART-TIME...

LOOOM...

Kimidori Sports

°°°

HUH?!

NOBODY KNOWS *YOUR* MUG! YOU GO!!

OH, THAT'S RIGHT!

THEY KNOW OUR FACES...

SIGH... THIS IS IT.

...SO WE CAN'T HELP.

HW OOOOO!!

KY OS HI N

DON'T LET THEM KNOW YOU'RE A SPY!!

N—NOT SO LOUD!

ALL RIGHT! TURF SHOES!

THANKS FOR COMING ALL THIS WAY TO...

KYOSHIN PO...

HELLO?

YOU'RE FROM DEIMON!

HEY!

YOU BET HE DID!!

OH, REALLY...?

...SPYING IS...

WRONG!

DEIMON'S WHAT?!

HE'S A SPY!!

A SPY!

WHAT?! HOW'D HE FIND ME OUT SO QUICKLY?!!

HE MUST'VE COME TO SPY!

ACKK! HELP M--

WUMP

WHAT'RE YOU DOING?

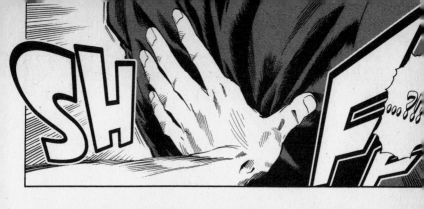

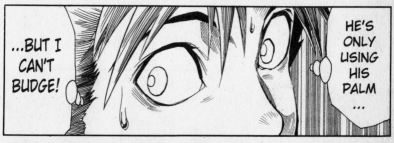

...BUT I CAN'T BUDGE!

HE'S ONLY USING HIS PALM...

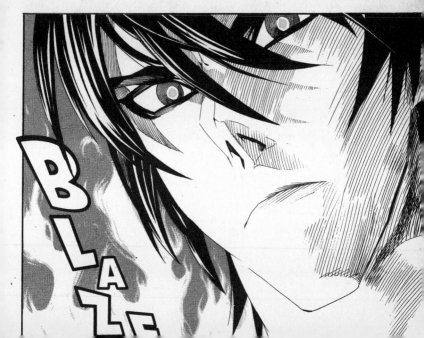

HE'S LATE.

HE CAN'T HAVE BEEN CAUGHT!!

...WHILE YOU WERE AT IT...

...YOU DELIVERED OUR SHOES FROM KIMIDORI SPORTS.

SO...

...YOU CAME TO VISIT AS MANAGER AND...

I APOLO- GIZE.

YOU CAME IN GOOD FAITH AND WE TREATED YOU LIKE A *SPY*.

N-NO... IT'S...

...ALL MY FAULT. THAT IS...

...I'M HAVING PANGS OF GUILT...

PANG
PANG

I THOUGHT YOU HATED DEIMON!

WHAT GIVES ALL OF A SUDDEN?

KAKEI'S SERVING TEA!!

HEY, WHAT'S UP?

I DON'T HATE DEIMON.

THE NAME DOESN'T REALLY MATTER.

...BUT I CAN'T STAND THAT FAKE EYESHIELD!

HE DELIVERED OUR CLEATS. AT LEAST THEIR MANAGER SENA IS A GOOD GUY...

...I WOULDN'T CARE **WHO** HE SAID HE WAS.

IF DEIMON'S NUMBER 21 WERE A TOP-NOTCH RUNNER...

I'M IN A FIX!

YIKES! UH... UM...

...IS NOTHING COMPARED TO THE DEVASTATING FORCE OF THE REAL EYESHIELD.

THE FAKE EYESHIELD'S RUNNING ABILITY...

BUT THIS IS DIFFERENT.

SLAM!

IF YOU'VE GOT THE STRENGTH TO EQUAL EYESHIELD...

...THEN BRING IT ON!!

A JOKER LIKE THAT CALLING HIMSELF EYESHIELD 21...

RATTLE RATTLE

...IS AN INSULT TO THE REAL ONE!

... GIVE THAT IMPOSTOR A MESSAGE FOR ME.

SENA...

TOP-NOTCH ...

FUNNY DUDE THAT KAKEI ...

HE FLIPS OUT WHENEVER IT'S ABOUT EYESHIELD!

IS HE STILL AT NOTRE DAME?

IS HE STILL A BIG STAR?

...IS STRONGER NOW THAN BEFORE?

DO YOU THINK THE REAL EYESHIELD...

NAH ...

...HE'S BACK IN JAPAN.

...WAS STUDYING ABROAD, AND ABOUT THE MYSTERY...

Kimidori Sports

...BEHIND THE *REAL* EYESHIELD 21?!

AND GET THIS...

...HE'S IN THE FALL TOURNAMENT!

HUH?! BUT WHY?

...ABOUT WHEN KAKEI...

WANNA HEAR?

WANNA HEAR...

High School Selection Guidance for Prospective Applicants!

OJO HIGH SCHOOL

Student Body: 1,070

Special Campus Facilities: Throne Room

Major Career Options after Graduation

OJO UNIVERSITY

CORONATION

Offers continuous education from junior high through university. The academic entrance requirements are extremely difficult, but the door is open to jocks through sports scholarships. However, the recent acceptance of a certain Mr. O has led to suggestions that a written test of some kind be required of such applicants.

Student Testimonial

Makoto Otawara

Ojo is great!

For example…

Um…**the food is great!**

And…**the lunches are great!**

And…oops, gotta fart! *BRRRIP!*

Now, what was I saying again…?

Oh, hey! Who's that Mr. O they're talking about?

UNIFORM

KAKEI WOULDN'T EVEN BE PLAYING TODAY...

...IF HE HADN'T MET *HIM* IN AMERICA!

...?

Chapter 112
The Phantom Footballer

...YOU WANNA KNOW ABOUT.

HE'S THE ONE...

THE *REAL*...

...EYE-SHIELD 21!!

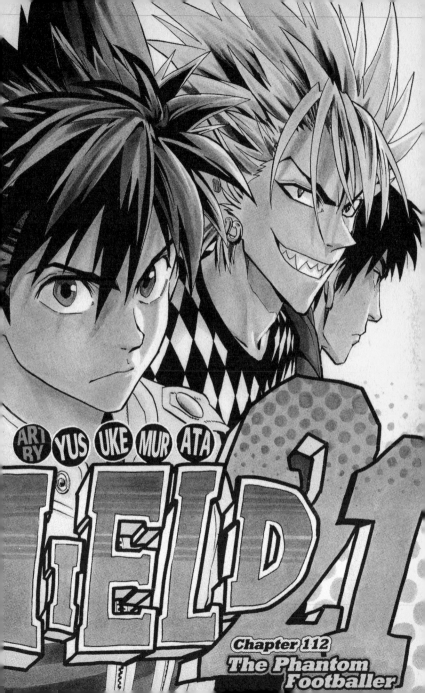

ART BY YUS UKE MUR ATA

Chapter 112
The Phantom
Footballer

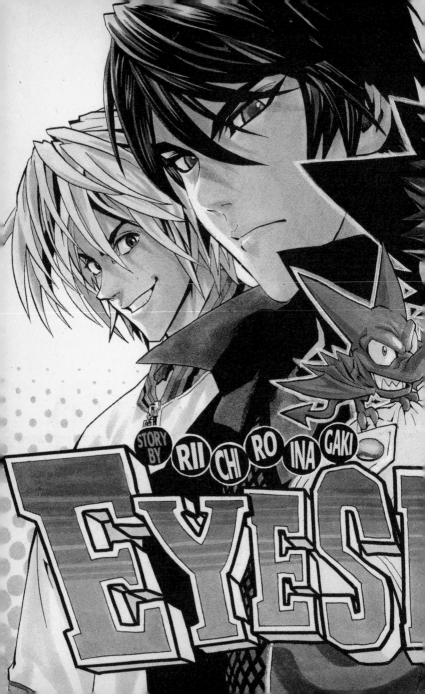

STORY BY RII CHI RO INA GAKI

EYES!

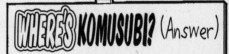

WHERE'S KOMUSUBI? (Answer)

Komusubi → Between the grocery store and the bookstore at the top of page 3.

Which character appears twice? → Monta. (He's in front of the grocery store on page 3 and in the café at the bottom of page 2.)

DID YOU FIND THEM ?!

KYOSHIN ELEMENTARY SCHOOL

FOUR YEARS AGO!!!

KWOOSH

WOW!!

KAKEI HAS THE BALL AGAIN!!

Riddell

※ABOUT 5'6"

HE WAS, LIKE, 170 CENTIMETERS TALL IN GRADE SCHOOL!!※

I HEAR HE WAS UNSTOPPABLE.

KAKEI WAS TALL FROM THE START...

...FOR A JAPANESE DUDE.

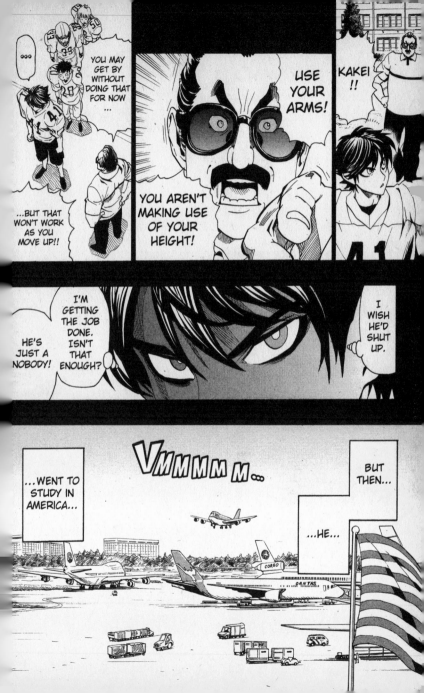

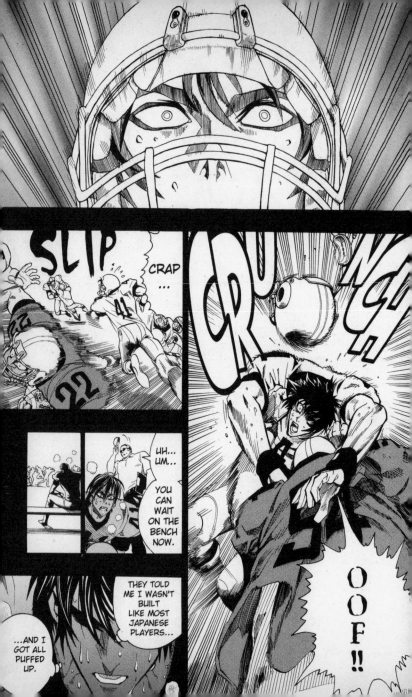

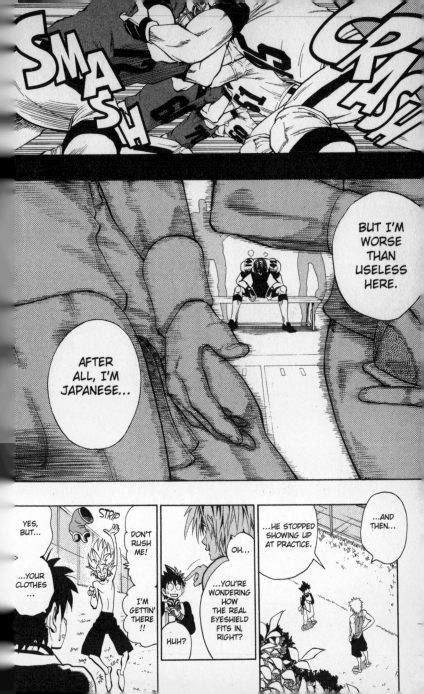

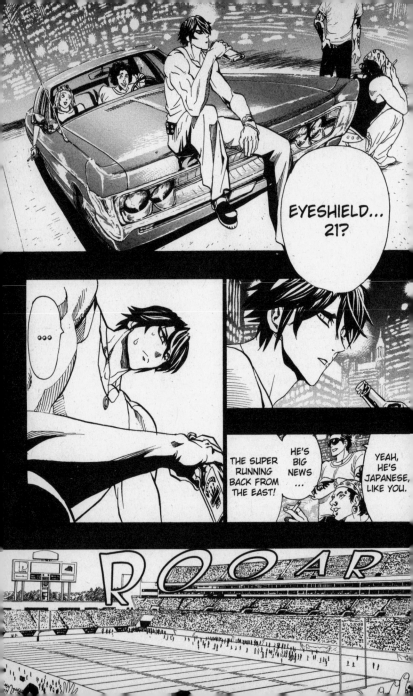

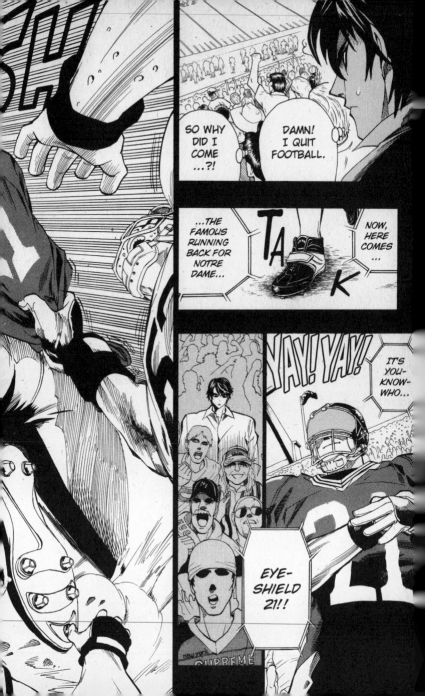

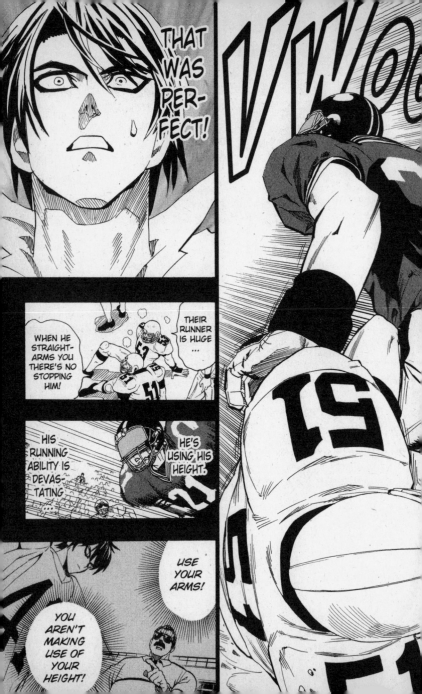

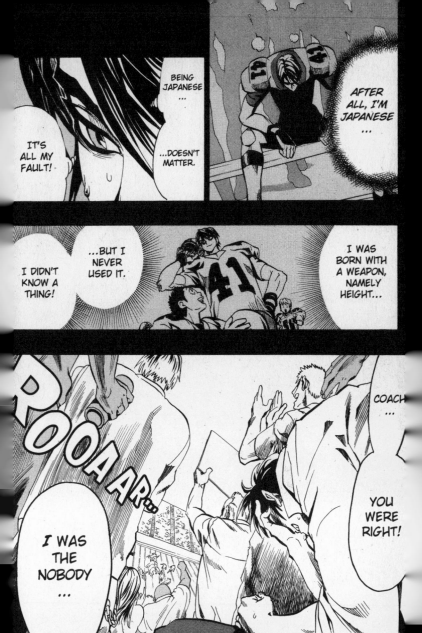

KAKEI!

T-TAKE IT... EASY!!

...IS OUR VERY OWN PHOENIX JUNIOR HIGH VERSUS...

...THE ONE AND ONLY NOTRE DAME!

PHOENIX 3

NOTREDAME 21

HERE TODAY...

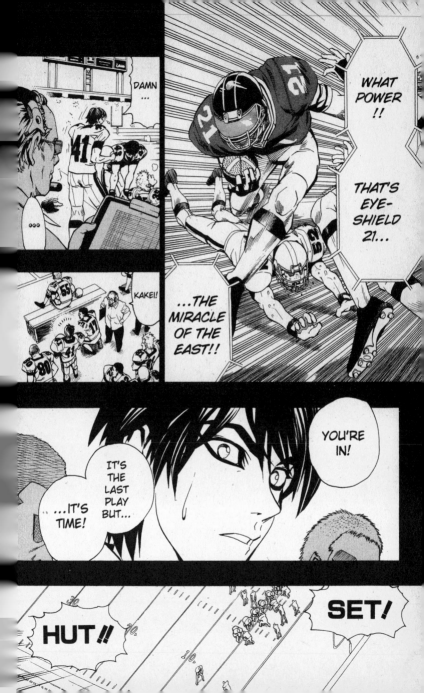

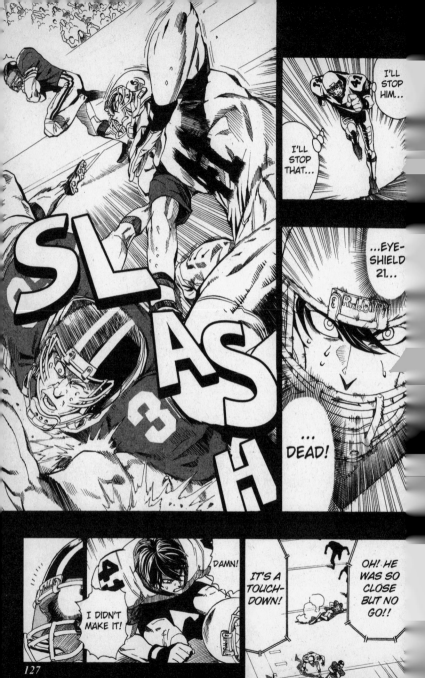

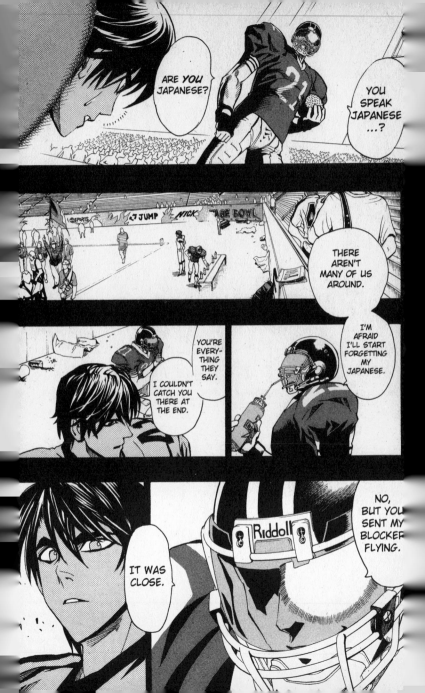

...IS IN AMERICA OR JAPAN...

AND WHETHER NEXT TIME...

RIGHT.

SORRY, SEE YOU NEXT TIME!

HEY, EYE-SHIELD.

THE MEETING'S GONNA START.

THAT'S A PROMISE!

...WE'RE GONNA FIGHT IT OUT FROM THE VERY START.

YES, BUT YOUR CLOTHES...

STRIP

THAT'S THE THING!

THAT'S WHERE THE MYSTERY BEGINS!

DIDN'T KAKEI ASK?

WHAT WAS HIS NAME...?

Kimidori Sports

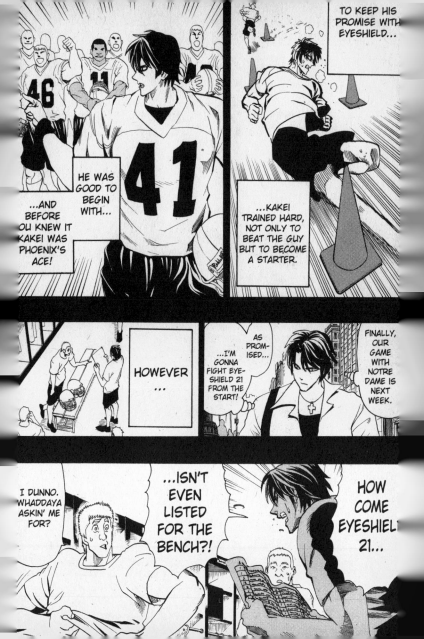

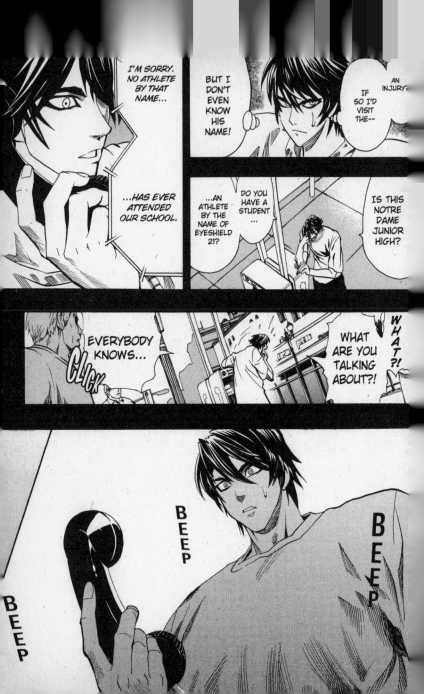

THAT'S IT?

HUH?

...THE GUY *MUST* BE IN THE NATIONAL TOURNAMENT.

SINCE THEY PROMISED TO FIGHT IT OUT...

KAKEI...

SPLOOSH

KAKEI BELIEVES EYESHIELD WILL KEEP HIS WORD.

...BELIEVED HIM!!

AND...

...IF HE IS IN THE TOURNAMENT...

I WONDER WHY EYESHIELD'S HIDING...

WHO IS...

...THE REAL EYE-SHIELD 21...?

...WE'LL PLAY HIM SOONER OR LATER.

IF WE JUST KEEP WINNING...

GLUB GLUB

DEIMON HAS LOTS OF SHORT DUDES...

...WHEREAS WE'VE GOT AN AWESOME HEIGHT ADVANTAGE.

SO WE'RE GONNA BEAT YOU! SORRY!

OMUSUBI OR SOMETHING.※

THAT TINY LINEMAN ON YOUR TEAM... WHAT'S-HIS-NAME?

I'LL TELL YOU ONE THING.

※A PLAY ON THE JAPANESE WORD FOR "RICE BALL"

THAT LITTLE SQUIRT'S IN FOR IT BIG TIME.

YOU SHOULD CUT HIM FROM THE TEAM.

UMPH

YOU'D PRACTICALLY BE ASKING ME TO FLATTEN HIM.

IF YOU DON'T, SORRY, BUT HE'LL BE MATCHED AGAINST ME.

BUT WE CAN'T DO THAT...

SPLAASH

WHERE ARE YOU GOING? HEY!

HEY, KOMU-SUBI...

...KOMU-SUBI AND THE REST OF US...

...HAVE TO PROVE OUR-SELVES!

JUST LIKE KAKEI SAID...

ooo

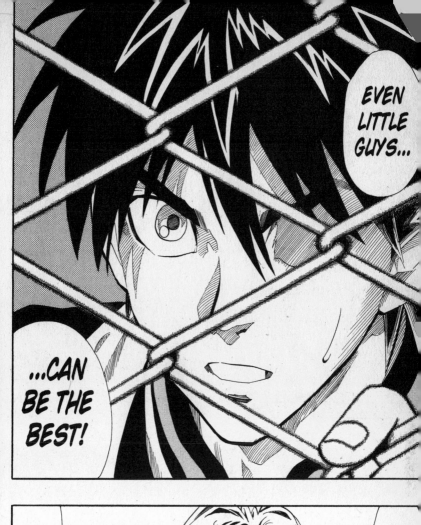

EVEN LITTLE GUYS...

...CAN BE THE BEST!

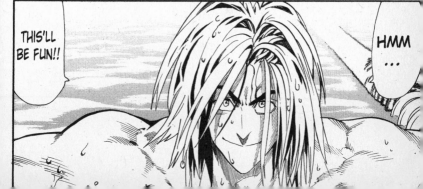

THIS'LL BE FUN!!

HMM...

ZOOM!

MONTA...

I HAVE AN IDEA.

...NOT A MANAGER!

THAT DUDE SHOULD BE A PLAYER...

ACKK!

WHAT DID I JUST SAY?!

SAY WHAT?!

A TRAINING METHOD FOR STOPPING KYOSHIN!!

KYOSHIN HIGH SCHOOL

Student Body: 1,170

Special Campus Facilities: 10 Elevators

Major Career Options after Graduation

UNIVERSITY	ELEVATOR COMPANY	OTHER

This mammoth school sits on very narrow land so it was built unbelievably tall. Students have come to believe that elevators are mankind's greatest invention, and thus flood elevator companies with job applications upon graduation.

Student Testimonial

Osamu Kobanzame

My impression of Kyoshin? Hmm, I'd say...super tall! Tuper Sall!

Oh...not that kind of impression? The school atmosphere? Oh, yeah...yeah! I was going to tell you about that.

The freshmen are super tall! Tuper Sall!

UNIFORM

SORRY, BUT HE'LL BE MATCHED AGAINST ME.

Chapter 113 Fists of Iron

NO-THING... IT'S JUST THAT...

WHAT IS IT, SENA?

YOU'D PRACTICALLY BE ASKING ME...

...TO FLATTEN HIM.

HE MUST HAVE HEARD...

...KOMU-SUBI LEFT IN A HURRY YESTERDAY.

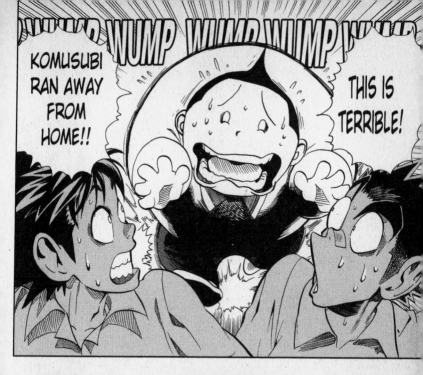

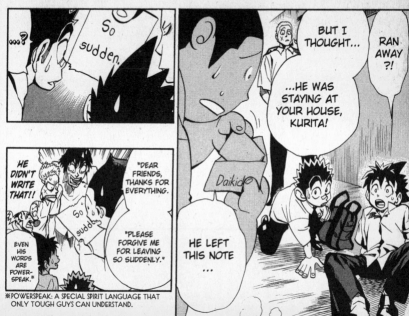

"I'M NO USE, SO I WON'T CAUSE YOU ANY MORE TROUBLE."

"THE TEAM IS BETTER OFF WITHOUT ME.

YOU SEE THIS TREE? IT WAS PLANTED WHEN MY GREAT-GREAT-GRANDFATHER WAS BORN.

•••

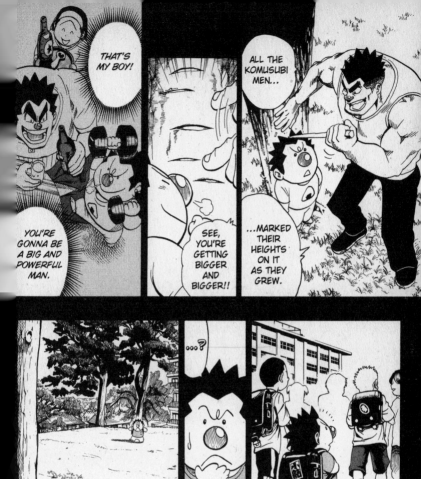

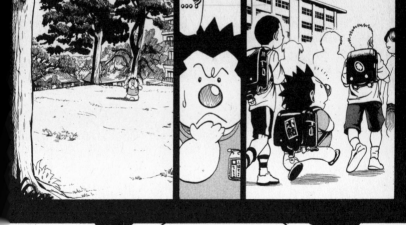

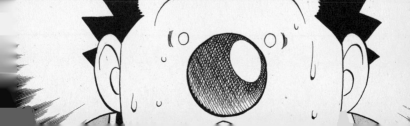

CUT
CUT

THAT LITTLE SQUIRT'S IN FOR IT BIG TIME.

YOU SHOULD CUT HIM FROM THE TEAM.

UMPH
UMPH

I'VE NEVER SEEN HIM HELPING OUT.

WHAT DO YOU MEAN, "KURITA'S FOLLOWER"?

THAT KID IS USELESS!

DING-DING

DING-DING...

WHERE DID DAMN FATTY JUNIOR GO?!

HE HASN'T COME HOME YET...

※POSTER: ¥10,000 ≈ ABOUT U.S. $85

○○○

BEEP

ME, TOO!

YEAH, I'LL COME WITH YOU!!

I'LL TAKE A JOG AND ...

...CHECK THE NEIGHBORHOOD!

TAK

TCH!

RIGHT BEFORE OUR GAME AGAINST KYOSHIN ...

HAH!

STUPID RED-NOSED FOOL!

HAVE YOU SEEN ↓

¥ 10.000

NOBODY CAN READ IT IF YOU DO THAT!

FWOOSH

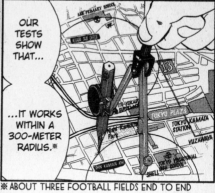

OUR TESTS SHOW THAT...

...IT WORKS WITHIN A 300-METER RADIUS.※

※ABOUT THREE FOOTBALL FIELDS END TO END

KURITA...

TRY HERE NEXT!

146

...SUUUUUBIIIII!!

KOOO MUUUUU...

BOOM

NEXT! ON TO THE NEXT SPOT!

...NOPE, NOT AROUND HERE...

WOO-OO-EE-EE!

AAUGH!!

THOMP!

OH! EVENING, MR. ISHIMARU, SIR.

I WAS SEARCHING FROM ABOVE.

RUSTLE

RUSTLE

RUSTLE

KOMU-SUBI...

...BUT HE CAN STILL DO A LOT!!

...MAY BE SHORT...

I'LL SCOUR THE TOWN ON FOOT.

GOTTA KEEP MOVING!!

H-HE'S GOING WILD...

CHIRP

CHIRP

UMPH

GNAW

GNAW

UMPH

I'LL GO VISIT...

...KOMUSUBI'S RELATIVES AND CHECK EVERY LEAD.

•••

SO YOU GO BACK AND GET EVERYONE TRAINING.

JR DEIMON STATION

I'LL KEEP LOOKING, HOWEVER LONG IT TAKES.

DOBU-ROKU-SENSEI SAID *THAT*?

UNH?

WHAT?!

HE'S GOING TO... *HANG* HIMSELF!!

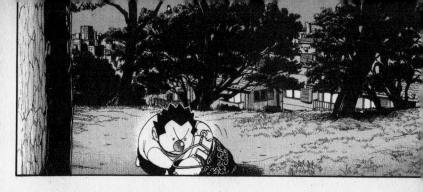

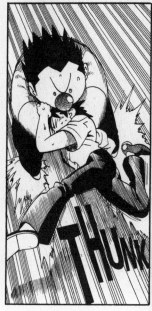

THUNK

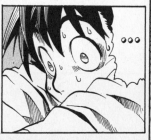

...

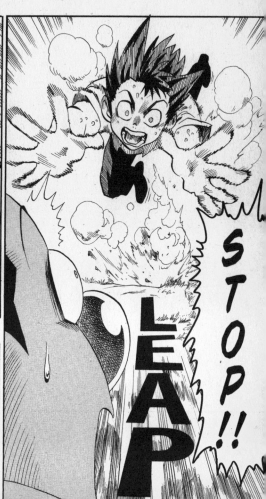

LEAP

STOP!!

KOMUSUBI, YOU AND THE OTHERS...

...ACT AS INCREDIBLE SHIELDS!

YOU'RE TRAINED TO BLOCK...

...NOT LIKE US BACKS.

YOU'RE AMAZING, NO QUESTION!

ANYONE HURT?

WAAAAAH! THANK GOODNESS! KOMUSUBI!

WE AREN'T THE DEVIL BATS...

...WITH-OUT YOU!

COME ON, KOMU-SUBI! COME BACK WITH US!

KCHAK

BUDDA

BUDDA

BUDDA

BUDDA

SWASH

SWASH

SWASH

THEY WENT BACK AND GOT THEM...

...SO THEY COULD LOOK FOR KOMUSUBI!

HUH?

I DON'T THINK THEY HAD THEIR BIKES AT SCHOOL...

WHAT'S THIS "I'M A NUISANCE" CRAP?!

DIE, SCUM !!

STOMP STOMP

WHAT'S THE BIG IDEA?!!

YOU THINK WE CAN ...

...BEAT KYOSHIN WITHOUT YOU?!

T....

IT'S ALL FALLING INTO PLACE.

LET HIM BE.

WHOA! HE'S BACK!!!

TRAINING !!!

BATHOMPPP!

...HEIGHT PLUS SPEED PLUS TECH-NIQUE!

TA I DAA

WE'RE THE VIRTUAL MIZU-MACHI!!

CHIRP

CHIRP

YEAH, I THOUGHT OF...

...A WAY TO TRAIN AGAINST KYOSHIN!

COMBINE EYE-SHIELD'S LEGS AND...

...MY MIRACLE HANDS TO GET...

THEY'RE ALL FRIGGIN' IDIOTS.

WHERE'S DOBU-ROKU-SENSEI?

WE'LL FIND YOU!

HANG IN THERE, KOMU-SUBI...

High School Selection Guidance for Prospective Applicants!

DEIMON HIGH SCHOOL

Student Body: 719

Special Campus Facilities: Several Armories

Major Career Options after Graduation

UNIVERSITY	EMPLOY-MENT	OTHER

Pawn for a certain Mr. H

The school values autonomy among its students and fosters a spirit of independence. At least that's how it turned out since no one could do anything about a certain Mr. H.

Despite this hands-off approach, there is hardly any trouble at the school. The students are actively involved in club activities and enjoy school life. Of course, it's impossible to act up under Mr. H's rule...but the result is that things seem to be going quite well.

Student Testimonial

Sena Kobayakawa

What? A word from me?!

Um...well...hello...

UNIFORM

Chapter 114 Komusubi's Last-Ditch Move

SET!

WAIT!

W-W-W...

STOP YOUR WHINING!

GOTTA GET TO SUMO CLUB OR I'LL GET YELLED AT FOR BEING LATE! *HUF HUF!*

HOW COULD I KNOW I'D BE A PRACTICE DUMMY?! *HUF HUF...*

ALL THIS FOR A FREE HONEY-LEMON DRINK...

YOU DO YOUR PART AND I'LL DO MINE!

WE'LL BE THE TWO-MAN VIRTUAL MIZU-MACHI!!

TREMBLE TREMBLE

THIS WILL NEVER WORK...

TREMBLE

TREMBLE

WOBBLE

WOBBLE

HUT!!

FORGET IT.

THIS WON'T WORK.

YOU FIGURED THAT OUT?!

NNGHACKK!!

WHAM

NO, *BECAUSE* THEY'RE TALL...

EVEN IF THEY'RE TALL...

HERE'S THE THING ABOUT THE LINE.

...THEY CAN BE TRIPPED UP.

IF YOU'RE SLOW AT THE TACHIAI, YOU'LL BE PUSHED BACK.※

※TACHIAI IS WHEN SUMO WRESTLERS FIRST
  CHARGE AT EACH OTHER.

PHYSICAL SIZE, DEADLY TECHNIQUE AND SPEED WON'T MATTER.

WE HIT 'EM BEFORE THEY'RE READY!

THAT'S IT!!

T...

WE'LL KICK THEIR BUTTS!!

TACHIAI!!

SUMO!! YEAH!!

SPEAKING OF A TACHIAI...

...AND I'M A PERSON!

WHAT A PAIN!

PEOPLE DON'T DO THINGS THAT ARE A PAIN...

OH...

HUH? YOU WANT ME TO TEACH YOU SUMO?

NO WAY! I MEAN...

CHECK OUT WHAT'S GOING ON THIS WEEK.

IF YOU WANT TO LEARN, WHY NOT TRY IT FOR REAL?

"...SUMO TOURNA-MENT"?!

"DEIMON SHOPPING MALL...

Deimon Shopping Mall

SUMO TOURNAMENT

Chapter 114

Komusubi's Last-Ditch Move

EYESHIELD 21

STORY BY RIICHIRO INAGAKI

ART BY YUSUKE MURATA

※BANNER: AMEFUTO STABLE ("STABLE" BEING A BAND OF SUMO WRESTLERS)

Annual
Deimon Shopping Mall Sumo Tournament

※A SUMO BATTLE CRY

HOORAY!
HOORAY!

GO DEIMON PIP-SQUEAKS!!

DOSU-KOI!!!※

BADABAM!

ACKK! ARE WE REALLY DOING THIS...?!

A QUICK TACHIAI IS IMPORTANT IN THE BACKFIELD, TOO!!

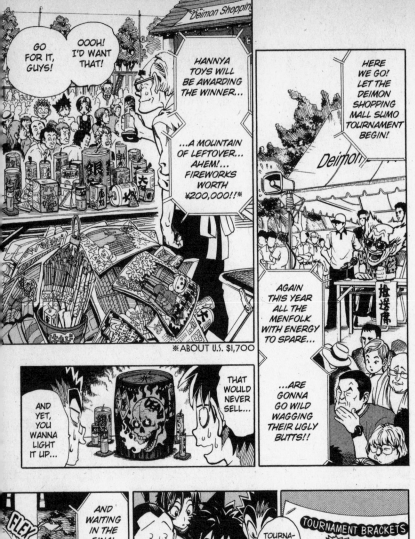
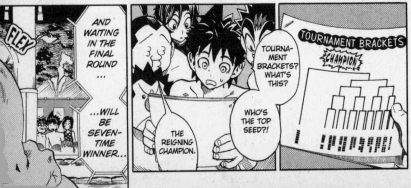

DA-DUM

...OJO HIGH SCHOOL'S...

MAKOTO OTAWARA!!

WHAAAAT?!

EVEN MORE SO THAN IN FOOTBALL!

GRRRRR

HE'S SO SCARY...!

WHADDAYA KNOW? IT'S THE FIRST-YEAR DEIMON BOYS!

WA HA HA!

YOU, TOO! YOU, TOO!

YOU GOT TIME FOR SUMO?

FALL TOURNAMENT QUARTERFINALS ARE TOMORROW AND YOU'RE HERE?

...LET'S BEGIN THE FIRST ROUND!!

AND NOW...

DOSU-KOI!!

LEAP

ACKK!!!

SHPAT

I'M GONNA GET EVEN FOR LOSING AT TOKYO TOWER.

HUH? MONTA'S FIRST?!

NOTE: SUMO WRESTLERS THROW SALT TO PURIFY THE RING.

RAHH

UMM... WHO SHOULD I CHEER FOR?

UNH!!

WHISH

VIP

BA BA BA BA BA BA BA BA BABA

WHOOOOOA!!

YOU'D THINK HIS LEGS WOULD BE GOOD FOR OTHER SPORTS BUT THEY'RE NOT.

GOOD THING YOU CHOSE FOOTBALL!

OUT OF BOUNDS! YOU'RE OUT AND... OUT AGAIN!

WHOOOOOOA!!

FIGHT!!

RAAHH!

TAKE YOUR POSITIONS!

THAT WAS GREAT, KOMUSUBI!!

WAY TO GO!!

SHH SHH SHH SHH

YAAAAAAY!!

WHAMMO

UMPH!!

I GOT ROPED INTO BEING A GUIDE, ALL FOR A FREE BANANA.

WALKING HOME IS SUCH A PAIN. *HUF HUF...*

HUM-DEE-DUM...

HUH?

NO, WELL... SORTA...

AREN'T YOU A SUMO WRESTLER? YOU LOOK IT.

KID, WHAT ARE YOU DOING HERE?

...OMOSA-DAKE!

HEY, THAT'S...

HUH?

HUH?

IF YOU'RE A WRESTLER, THEN PUT ON YOUR BELT AND GET OUT THERE!

OR YOU'LL BE DISQUAL-IFIED!!

UNH?

HOW DID THIS HAPPEN?!

AW, MAN...

READY!

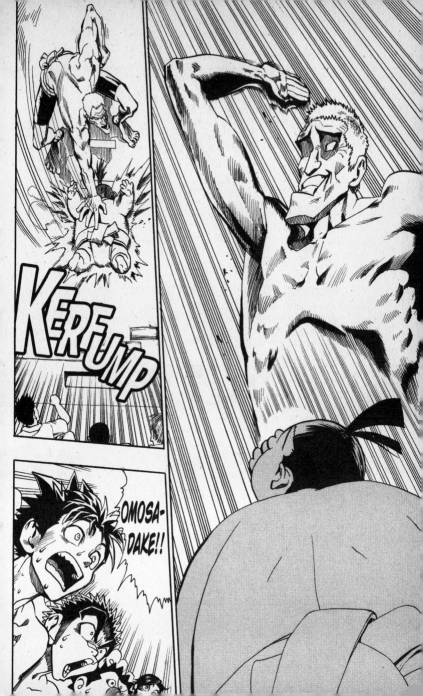

CHI CHING

I'M NUMBER O-O-O-NE!!!

...

AND IMMA-TURE!

THAT OLD GUY...

...SURE IS TALL!

NO MORE SHRIMPS, PLEASE.

WHOOSH
WHOOSH

IT'S *VERY* BORING!

WH OOo SH

NNGH-YAH!

THIS IS PERFECT!

HEY, KOMU-SUBI...

JUST PRETEND THE OLD GUY IS MIZUMACHI...

...AND TAKE HIM OUT!

RAAH!

TOURNAMENT BRACKETS Deimon Shopping Mall Sumo Tournament

THE TOURNA-MENT HAS ENTERED ITS FINAL STAGES!

THE FINAL MATCH DRAWS NEAR!

YOU CAN DO IT!!

IS THIS ALL RIGHT ?!

WOW! LOOK AT THE HEIGHT DIFFERENCE!

FACE OFF!

NOT AGAIN.

SIGH

TAKE YOUR POSITIONS!

ANOTHER SHRIMP, ANOTHER EASY FIGHT!!

THE TACHIAI!

GRRRRR

WE HIT 'EM BEFORE THEY'RE READY...

...PHYSICAL SIZE WON'T MATTER.

WE'LL KICK THEIR BUTTS!!

WHOOM

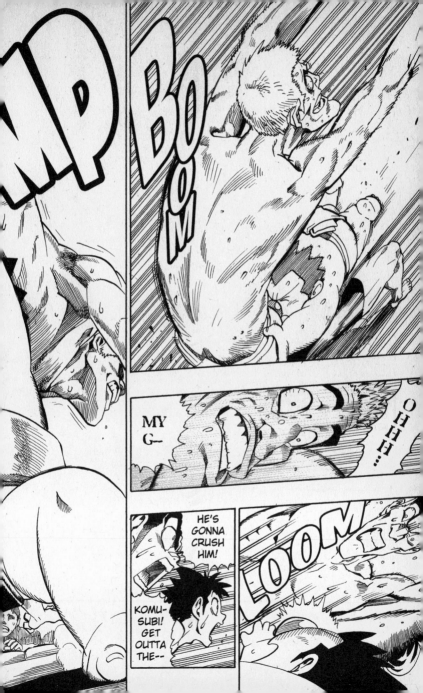

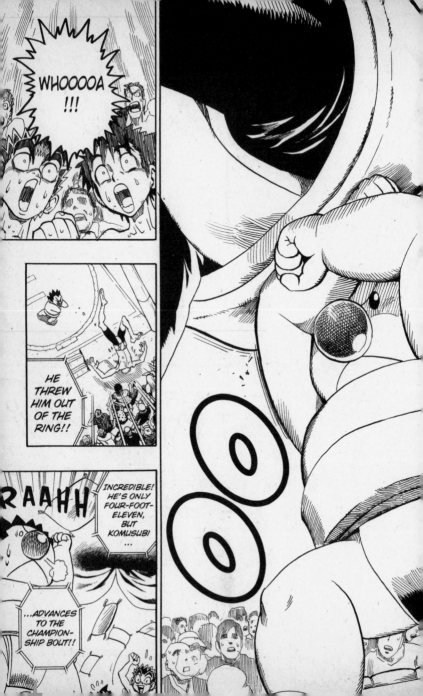

WA HA HA!

GOOD JOB, DEIMON PIP-SQUEAKS!

BUT I WON'T LET YOU WIN!

AND NOW...

...IT'S TIME FOR THE FINAL BATTLE AGAINST OTAWARA!!

R—AAHH!

SLAM!

CAN KOMU-SUBI...

...OVER-COME HIS SIZE...

...AND BRING DOWN THE UNDEFEATED YOKOZUNA OTAWARA?!※

※YOKOZUNA: TITLE FOR THE HIGHEST RANK IN SUMO.

BA BUMP

BA BUMP

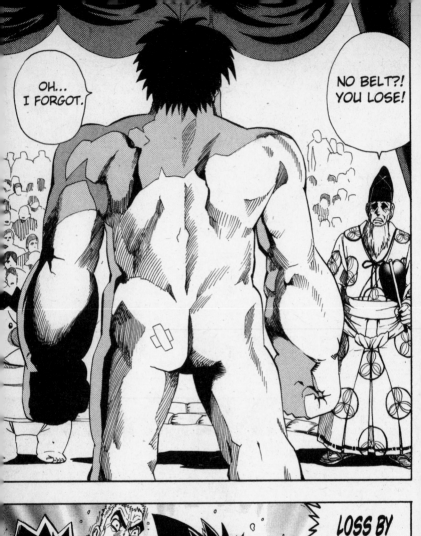

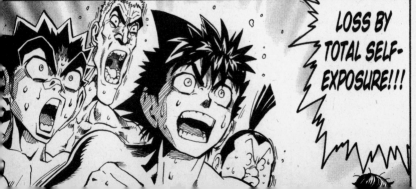

○ Investigation File #035

Find out what he used to look like!

LAZY FUTOSHI OMOSADAKE BELONGS TO THE SUMO CLUB. I'VE HEARD THAT HIS EYES LOOK THE WAY THEY DO BECAUSE HE FINDS OPENING THEM TO BE A PAIN. WHAT DID HIS EYES LOOK LIKE ORIGINALLY?

S.K., Shizuoka Prefecture

NO WAY!

Futoshi Omosadake, age 12

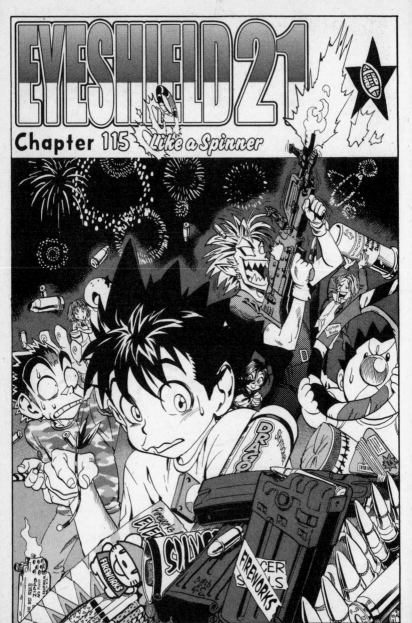

EYESHIELD 21

Chapter 115 *Like a Spinner*

ONLY FIVE MINUTES LEFT...

...IN THE PLAY-CARD MEMORY TESTS!

NO CHEATING!!

NNGH SKRK! SCRIBBLE SKRK SKRK SKRK ZZZ SIGH SCRIBBLE
AH HA HA SKRK SKRK SKRK SKRK SKRK
SCRIBBL SKRK HAH? HAH? HAAH?

ANYONE BELOW 80 POINTS GETS THE DEATH PENALTY!

K-CHK

SHWIP SHWIP

GRADING THIS MANY IS HARD.

I KNOW, BUT THE KYOSHIN GAME'S TOMORROW.

IF WE DON'T KNOW THE PLAYS...

ACKK! DONE!

THAT WAS HARD...

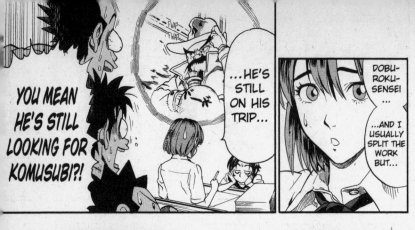
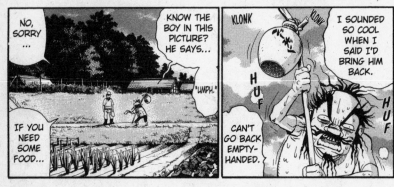
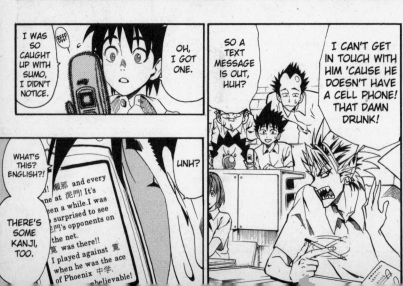

FOCUS FOCUS

BLUR WATT...? BLUR

...JEREMY WATT.

IT SAYS THE SENDER IS...

HE'S WITH THE AMERICAN TEAM!

THE NASA ALIENS!!

KAKEI WAS THERE!!

KAKEI SHUN
筧 駿

I WAS SURPRISED TO SEE DEIMON'S OPPONENTS ON THE NET.

DEAR SENA AND EVERYONE AT DEIMON. IT'S BEEN A WHILE.

HI THERE!

HE WAS UNBELIEVABLE!

HE STOPPED ME EVERY TIME USING HIS HEIGHT AND LONG REACH.

I PLAYED AGAINST KAKEI WHEN HE WAS THE ACE OF...

...PHOENIX JUNIOR HIGH.

I SAW HIM FROM THE BENCH.

PANTHER, YOU REMEMBER KAKEI, RIGHT?

AFTER THAT, I LEARNED EVERYTHING ABOUT JAPAN!

SAMURAI ARE AWESOME!

I'M SURE HE'LL BE BRILLIANT IN HIGH SCHOOL, TOO.

AND STILL IN JUNIOR HIGH.

HE WAS AMAZING ALL RIGHT.

SIMPLE-MINDED, AS ALWAYS.

...HOW A MAN NOT ENDOWED WITH AN AWESOME BUILD...

...CONFRONTS A GENIUS WHO IS SO ENDOWED!

SHOW ME, SENA...

BONK

AT TOMORROW'S PLAYOFF...

...WE FACE DEIMON, SO LET'S REVIEW HOW WE'RE GOING TO TAKE *DEM ON.*

Kyoshin High School

...FLUFFY... I MEAN, A *TOUGHIE!*

HE'S... UH... BY WAY OF ANALYSIS...

...THERE'S KAKEI'S RIVAL, THE FAKE EYESHIELD 21!

BIP

OKAY, FIRST...

SO 21'S A WUSS!

BUT PRAISE HIM AND KAKEI'LL FREAK!

MACH SU-PER! SPEED!

HE'S RABID! I MEAN... *RAPID!*

CAN A FAST PAPER AIRPLANE...

...BREAK THROUGH A BRICK WALL?

...BUT HIS BODY IS A MERE SCRAP OF PAPER.

HIS LEGS ARE A THREAT...

IF WE CHARGE IN AND SURROUND HIM, HE'LL BE NO THREAT.

DEIMON DOESN'T HAVE ANY GREAT BLOCKERS...

...TO COVER HIS LACK OF POWER.

HAH!

LEAVE IT TO ME!

IN THE DEIMON LINE...

...THERE'S A FATAL, LITTLE DUDE-SIZED HOLE!

YEAH! THAT'S IT!

WHAT A BRILLIANT SUMMARY OF MY STUNNING ANALYSIS!!

WE CAN RELY ON MIZUMACHI'S CONFIDENCE!

NOW ABOUT OUR LINE...

ALL RIGHT! DOWN WITH THE KYOSHIN POSEIDONS!!

THEY'RE THE ONES WHO STOPPED HASHIRATANI AND ONIHEI.

TOMORROW DEFINITELY WON'T...

...BE THE WAY IT'S BEEN SO FAR.

LET'S SHOOT 'EM OFF TOGETHER LATER!

NO, NO... NO MORE FIREWORKS!!

HUH?

TRAIN TO THE SOUND OF SPINNERS?

TACHIAI!!

WHIZZ WHIZZ WHIZZ

PO W!!!

KA...

OW!

BONK

HEY
...

I KNEW
YOU'D BE
HERE.

EYESHIELD
...21?

Middle School
2087१

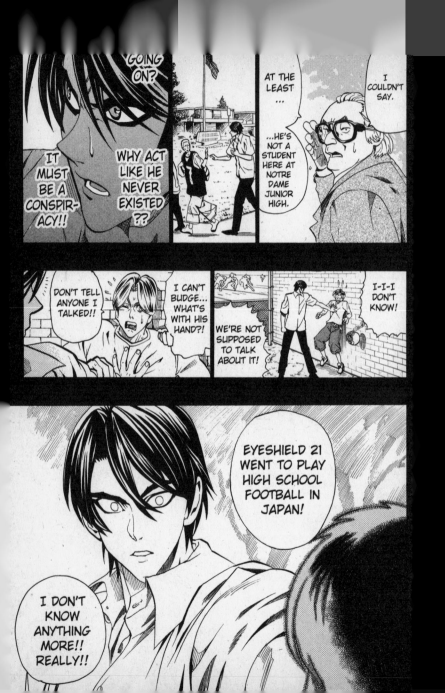

RATTLE

YOU IDIOT! WHAT'RE YOU DOING? THAT'S DANGEROUS!

RATTLE

TAK

MIZU-MACHI! GET DOWN!

YOU SAID THAT.

HIGH PLACES FEEL GREAT!

YOU KNOW WHAT?

HWOOO...

THAT'S WHAT YOU TOLD ME...

WE'LL WIN IT ALL WITH OUR HEIGHT!

...SO I SWITCHED TO FOOT-BALL.

ASIDE FROM KOBANZAME AND THE BACKS...

...ALL OF OUR PLAYERS ARE OVER FIVE-FOOT-ELEVEN.

OUR HEIGHT IS OUR BEST WEAPON!

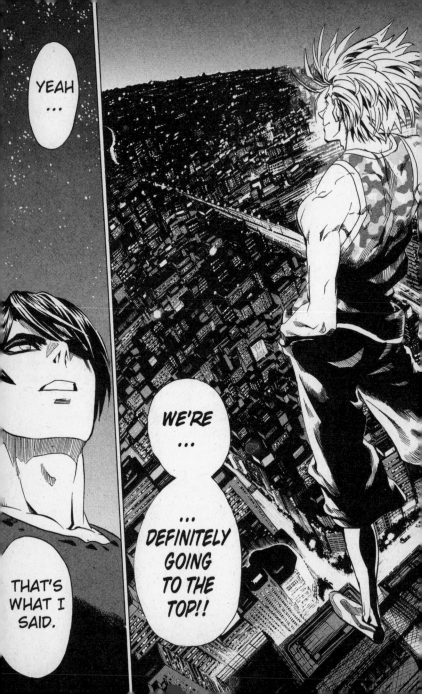

THERE'S NO SUCH PLACE IN TOKYO!!

IT SAYS, "BURSTING WITH DANGER."

"DO NOT USE WITHIN HALF A MILE OF ANY OBJECT."

DON'T LIGHT IT!

DA-DUM

WHAT ABOUT THIS ONE...?

THEY'RE SMALL AND JUST SPIN AROUND ON THE GROUND...

...SO THEY DON'T MAKE THE SAME IMPACT AS THE *BIGGER* SKYROCKETS.

...I LIKE THE SPINNERS.

THE FLASHY ONES ARE NICE BUT ...

I THINK THAT'S COOL, DON'T YOU?

BUT AFTER THEY SPIN ALL OVER...

...THEY FINISH WITH A BANG!

EVEN THOUGH THEY'RE SMALL...

...THEY GET THE JOB DONE!!

YEAH.

THAT DAMN FATTY JUNIOR...

...IS WITHOUT A DOUBT A KEY TO WINNING.

DON'T WORRY!

WITH YOU AND ME BOTH, IT'LL BE EASY!

TOMORROW'S THE BIG GAME.

TO BE HONEST... ...DEIMON IS TOUGH.

BUT...

...WE'RE STILL OVERWHELMINGLY TALL.

DEIMON'S OFFENSE IS FORMIDABLE...

TOMORROW...

...IT'S DEIMON VERSUS KYOSHIN.

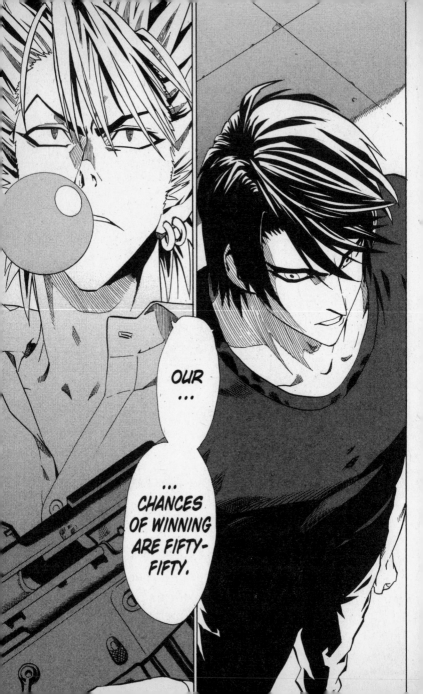

FLIK

WANNA DO 'EM ALL?

WOW! WE STILL HAVE SO MANY!

WHIZZ BA-CA-BAM

IT'S A SPINNER FESTIVAL!!

AAAUGH!!

THAT'S ALL, GUYS!

A USELESS PURPOSE FOR HIS CATCHING SKILLS!!

Fireworks

COUNTER-ATTACK! C'MON!

DANGEROUS FOOL!!

PAPA POW

AHAA-EEEK-HAA!!

WHIZ-BA-BA-BAP

AH HA HA!

ANOTHER FOOL BITES THE DUST ...

I CAN HOLD A HUNDRED AT ONCE!!

PSSSH...

DEAD

FLASH

RRRUMBBLE

THAT SOUNDS BAD...

B'A SHOOM SHOOM SHOOM SHOOM

AAA AGGH HH!!

SO IT'S FIFTY-FIFTY.

LET'S WIN...

...TOMOR-ROW'S GAME!!

SPARK SPARK

BOOM

I'M FIRED UP!!

KOMU-SUBI...

GOT IT? TODAY'S FIRE DIDN'T HAPPEN.

THIS COULD GET US DISQUALIFIED...

IT'S THE BIG GAME!!

THE NEXT MORNING, THE DEIMON DEVIL BATS...

...WILL FACE JAPAN'S GREATEST LINE.

End of Volume 13:
Who Is the Real Eyeshield 21?

○ Investigation
○ File #036

Get your hands on a manga by Togano!!

I KNOW TOGANO LOVES MANGA, AND I SAW HIM DRAWING ONE ON THE "COMIC STRIP HALFTIME" PAGES IN VOLUME 12. I WANT TO READ HIS WORK!!

K.G., Yamaguchi Prefecture

I STOLE AN UNFINISHED MANGA FROM HIM!

Summary of Togano's Manga

The main character, Shozo, dreams of becoming a master of kenpo, the Chinese version of boxing. He can stretch his arms like rubber and control his ki. He has psychic powers and can also use ninjutsu, which makes him incredibly powerful. He excels at tennis, baseball and basketball, and his slamdunks are forceful. On top of that, he has recently improved his skills as a lineman in football.

Investigation File #037

Investigate what Deimon's players like in a girl!

M.H., Nagano Prefecture and elsewhere

WE'LL ASK 'EM ONE BY ONE.

LET'S START WITH MONTA.

THERE'S NOT MUCH SPACE SO KEEP IT SHORT.

WHAT? MY TYPE?!

I CAN'T BE BOTHERED WITH A QUESTION LIKE THAT WHEN WE'RE ABOUT TO WIN THE TOURNAMENT!! BUT IF I HAD TO SAY...I MEAN, REALLY HAD TO SAY...NOT THAT I'M INTERESTED IN LOVELY-DOVEY...BUT IF I HAD TO SAY...I GUESS SHE'D BE KIND AND...HOW SHOULD I PUT IT?...SMART AND PRACTICAL...LIKE...MAMORI! B-B-BUT I'M NOT POINTING AT ANYONE IN PARTICULAR! HEH HEH... BUT WHEN A MAN'S FIGHTING ALONE, HAVING SOMEONE THERE WITH HIM--

THAT'S IT! WE'RE OUT OF ROOM!

PLEASE BE PATIENT!!

WE CAN'T ANSWER EVERY QUERY...

Send your queries for Devil Bat 021 here!!

Devil Bat 021
Shonen Jump Advanced/Eyeshield 21
c/o VIZ Media, LLC
P.O. Box 77010
San Francisco, CA 94107

Deluxe Biographies
of the Supporting Cast

Kanagushi

He's an expert at reading people's intentions from their gestures. Because of this skill, he tends to look down on others.

When his father would lecture him about his attitude, Kanagushi would say, "Shee-hee-hee! It's so easy! I can read people in an instant! Dad, you're thinking about slapping m--. *Ouch!!*"

As is often the case, he got his face slapped. *In life, reading others' intentions is frequently no help at all.*

Jonan Giants Cheerleaders

Compared to these girls, the players are scrawny! The guys do have some grit, because *they're afraid of what the girls will do to them if they lose...*

Kimidori Sports

This is a famous old shop in the neighborhood. The owner recently started one of those trendy point-card systems.

You get one point for every ¥1,000 you spend there.* It seems that once you collect 100 points you get an *original postcard*. Needless to say, nobody is collecting.

※¥1,000 is about U.S. $9. Multiply this by 100.

Tall, Old Guy at the Sumo Tournament

He's the *ozeki* of Deimon Shopping Mall--this being the sumo rank just below yokozuna (the top rank).
The old man will go all out against anyone!!

Kids in *kindergarten* who've asked him to play sumo have been sent *flying!* Afterward, he says, "Easy fight!" and *roars with laughter!* To a kid in kindergarten! Well, fair is fair…

Yakiniku Minotaur

This place is famous for the staff's rigorous morning training. Recently, "jumping dogeza" was added to the program. [Dogeza is a deep bow. See vol. 7, pp. 123-124 for more on this.]

This was so that the staff can beg kids like that pointy-headed boy to leave if he ever comes back for their all-you-can-eat buffet.

Sengoku Samurai Coach

He has a habit of saying, *"If we lose, I'll commit harakiri!!"* Not that he ever has, mind you.

Another of his favorite sayings is, *"My word is my bond!!"* Not that it ever is, mind you.

The Magician

OOOH

MAGIC IS...

...AN ESSENTIAL PART OF EVERY PARTY!

OOOOH

AND NOW, FOR OUR NEXT TRICK...

SPOON BENDING!!

READY...

...GO!!

OOOOH

THAT'S NOT MAGIC!!

First published in *GAG Special 2005 Extra*

The Devil Bat Pirates

FIRE!! PIRATES!

SHH SHH

ACKK!

THERE ARE ONLY TEN DEVIL BAT PIRATES.

ACK!

ACK!

WHAT'S WITH THOSE CUTS?!

SWOOSH

BOING

KCH

BAKOOM

BASHOON

THEY TURN OUT TO BE QUITE STRONG.

First published in *Weekly Shonen Jump*, combined issue, nos. 22 and 23 (2003).

Santa's Light-Speed Trio

The Devil's Present

I WONDER IF I CAN DELIVER THESE ALL TODAY!

IF ONLY THERE WERE A SPEEDY SANTA...

PRESENTS! PRESENTS!

OH! SANTA!

GREAT! IT'S GOOD TO HAVE FRIENDS!!

WE'LL HELP YOU!

EH?!

I'LL JUST DELIVER THEM WHEREVER.

I CAN'T READ THE ADDRESSES, THEY'RE IN JAPANESE!

THEY'RE TOO... HEAVY...

GAAHHH! WHAT A DISASTER!!

PROBABLY TO USE THE BATHROOM...

WHAT DID THEY COME FOR?

205

First published in *Weekly Shonen Jump*, combined issue, nos. 4 and 5 (2004).

BOW DOWN
BEFORE THE GIANT GODS!
Smash through Japan's Greatest Line!!
Vol. 14
On Sale June 2007!!

Story: Riichiro Inagaki
Art: Yusuke Murata

Chief: Akira Tanaka
STAFF: Takahiro Hiraishi
Kentaro Kurimoto
Akira Nishikawa
Yukinori Kawaguchi
Masayuki Shiomura
Sanmi Yi

EYESHIELD 21

EYESHIELD 21

Vol 13: Who Is the Real Eyeshield 21?

The SHONEN JUMP ADVANCED Manga Edition

STORY BY RIICHIRO INAGAKI
ART BY YUSUKE MURATA

Translation/Craig & Hime Kingsley, HC Language Solutions, Inc.
English Adaptation/John Werry, HC Language Solutions, Inc.
Touch-up Art & Lettering/James Gaubatz
Cover and Graphic Design/Sean Lee
Editor/Yuki Takagaki

Managing Editor/Frances E. Wall
Editorial Director/Elizabeth Kawasaki
VP & Editor in Chief/Yumi Hoashi
Sr. Director of Acquisitions/Rika Inouye
Sr. VP of Marketing/Liza Coppola
Exec. VP of Sales & Marketing/John Easum
Publisher/Hyoe Narita

Published by VIZ Media, LLC
P.O. Box 77010
San Francisco, CA 94107

SHONEN JUMP ADVANCED Manga Edition
10 9 8 7 6 5 4 3 2 1
First printing, April 2007

www.viz.com

PARENTAL ADVISORY
EYESHIELD 21 is rated T+ for Older Teen and is
recommended for ages 16 and up. It contains
graphic fantasy violence and crude humor.

THE WORLD'S MOST
CUTTING-EDGE MANGA

SHONEN JUMP
ADVANCED

www.shonenjump.com

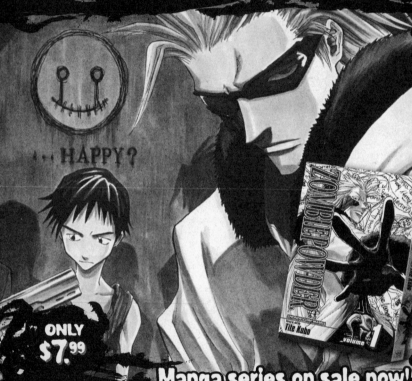

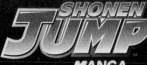

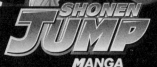

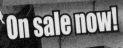

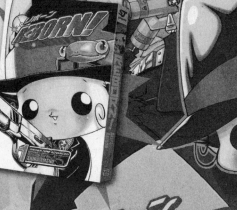

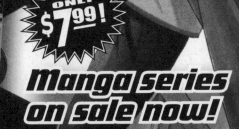
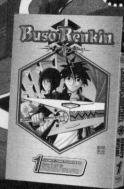

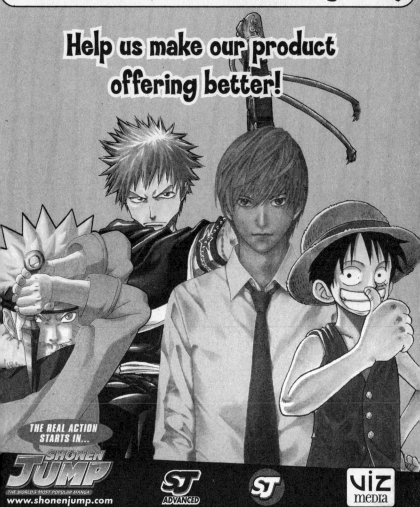

W9-DAJ-745

Date: 11/2/11

GRA 741.5 EYE V.13
Inagaki, Riichiro.
Eyeshield 21. Who is the real
Eyeshield 21? /